# THE STORY OF TUNNELS

*Frontispiece.*—Under the brilliant glare of photographers' lights, construction takes on a dramatic setting in the Lincoln Tunnel. (*Courtesy of The Port of New York Authority.*)

# THE
# STORY OF TUNNELS

BY
**ARCHIBALD BLACK**
*Author of "The Story of Bridges," Etc.*

*New York* **WHITTLESEY HOUSE** *London*
McGRAW-HILL BOOK COMPANY, INC.

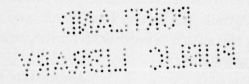

## PUBLISHED BY WHITTLESEY HOUSE
A division of the McGraw-Hill Book Company, Inc.

*Printed in the United States of America by The Maple Press Co., York, Pa.*

# Preface

THIS book takes the form of an illustrated history of tunneling, written entirely for the non-technical reader. For obvious reasons, the account is confined to those tunnels which are of most general interest. All facts and figures have been checked with the greatest of care, in a belief that the reader has a right to expect accuracy equaling that of technical works.

For assistance in commenting upon and correcting the text, the author is indebted to Mr. Ole Singstad, Chief Engineer of the New York City Tunnel Authority and formerly Chief Engineer of the Holland Tunnel, to Col. C. S. Gleim, Engineer of Construction for The Port of New York Authority, and to his brother, Mr. D. R. Black, formerly structural engineer on tunnel construction for Patrick McGovern, Inc. To his wife, Dorothy E. Black, the author is indebted for criticism and many helpful suggestions.

ARCHIBALD BLACK.

GARDEN CITY, N. Y.

# Contents

# CONTENTS

X

# CONTENTS

# List of Illustrations

## LIST OF ILLUSTRATIONS

xiv

## LIST OF ILLUSTRATIONS

XV

# THE STORY OF TUNNELS

# Chapter I

# Tunnels of the Ancients

========================================

*The Earliest Tunnel in History.*

MORE than 4,000 years ago, a blazing tropical sun beat
down upon the naked backs of toiling slaves, their
skins burned to a bronze black from long exposure. At
the bottom of a great trench dug out of the muddy bed
of the Euphrates, they labored incessantly from sun-
rise to sundown while the waters of the river—reduced
to small volume by the dry season—flowed sluggishly
through the temporary channel into which they had
been diverted to make the construction possible. Under
the lash of driving overseers, an amazing structure was
taking form. Walls of brick were rising from the bottom
of the trench, with portions already reaching their full
height and arching over to form a closed passage. Like
an army of ants, the workers swarmed over the dry bed
of the river, some hurrying down into the trench carrying supplies of brick or the dark asphalt that would
serve to bind these bricks into a solid wall. Others were
building up the brick walls, and still others were moving
back the river-bed material to cover over the completed
portions. They were building a passageway under the

3

river—an undertaking entirely without precedent and truly in keeping with the greatness of Babylon, metropolis of the Universe. Where the tunnel passed under its bed the great river was about 600 feet wide; from end to end the complete passage would be more than 3,000 feet long. Built to connect the Royal Palace with the Temple of Jupiter on the opposite bank, it would provide a passage twelve feet wide and fifteen feet high, running right beneath the river that separated the two parts of this tremendous city. Never before had builders attempted such a daring experiment. Babylon the Great was again making history!

Such was the earliest tunnel recorded by history—with the manner of its building reconstructed from our present knowledge of Babylonian methods and materials. This was, most likely, far from being the first tunnel; the very boldness of the undertaking points to previous experience of some kind. For that matter, Nature herself antedated Man as a builder of tunnels. And those many caves throughout the World, so widely publicized as tourist points of interest, are just some examples of Nature's own tunneling. The Babylon Tunnel was mentioned by Diodorus Siculus, the early Sicilian historian who wrote a universal history of the world before the Christian era; he referred to it as having been built under the direction of Semiramis, the Queen of Assyria whose life has become so entwined with fable that certain historians even doubt the authenticity of her existence. Regardless of whether or not Semiramis really existed, however, there is enough evidence in the way of history to warrant the belief that this tunnel was actually built. Thus it has become accepted by present-day engineers as the first under-river tunnel ever constructed, the date being fixed as about 2180 to 2160 B.C. It is startling to note that this tunnel was big enough to pass a subway train and considerably larger in area than some of our modern rapid transit tunnels under rivers. Evidently it was an amazing achievement for the period. Indeed, it would have been an amazing achievement for many generations later. For it was not until the Thames Tunnel of 1842—*more than* 4,000 *years later*—that history had occasion to record the successful completion of another tunnel built in the soft ground of a river bed!

Today we can find no visible remains of this largest city of ancient times; its ruins lie completely covered by the drifted sands of twenty-five centuries. In that part of Asia which is now called Irak Arabi, we find the town of Hillah, believed by archaeologists to mark the site of ancient Babylon. About forty years ago the Germans sent an expedition to explore the mounds in this area, but the vast amount of sand, and the limited funds available to pay for moving it, became a severe restriction. In spite of this, some interesting discoveries were made. The "fabulous" wall of Babylon was unearthed at one point and found to be of double construction with sand and gravel fill between, making the total width 136½feet; its top lay more than twenty-

two feet below the surface. The greatest mound, within
the fifteen-mile square that was occupied by the
ancient city, rises nearly 200 feet and is topped by
ruins which are believed to be those of the Temple of
Belus, mentioned in the Bible as the "Tower of Babel."
This astounding structure is supposed to have been
about 625 feet high—about the same as a modern
fifty-story skyscraper!

## Tunneling in Warfare.

From Babylon we come to tunneling in warfare, an
application which began at an early date when attack-
ing armies used tunnels to provide a means for passing
under the walls of a besieged city. In other cases, the
attackers tunneled under the walls to cause their
collapse and hence open a path into a city. The fall of
Jericho (mentioned in the Bible) was most likely
accomplished by tunneling under its walls, the march-
ing armies and blare of trumpets serving to divert attention from the true means of attack. These applications
of tunneling reached a high point with the Greeks and
Romans, although they were far from being the first
tunnel builders.

Tunnels have also figured in warfare in still another
form—that of providing a source of water supply which
is under cover and hence safeguarded from enemy
interruption. King Hezekiah of Judah is supposed to
have built a tunnel to carry water into Jerusalem from
a spring outside of the city, for the purpose of assuring

a safe supply for its inhabitants upon the approach, or threatened approach, of the Assyrian Army. This tunnel must have been constructed in the eighth century B.C., and the legend is borne out by the discovery—described by the Palestine Exploration Fund in its 1881–1883 reports—of an ancient tunnel running about 600 feet between the Pool of the Virgins and the Pool of Siloam, near Jerusalem. There is not full agreement as to the date of this tunnel, some placing it at Hezekiah's time, others saying that it might well date back to Solomon. But, regardless of its exact date, the tunnel is interesting because of its early age. Running somewhat in the form of a letter "S," it is about 600 feet long although the two pools are only about 111 feet apart. The tunnel is small (averaging only about two feet in width) and was evidently worked from the two ends, which came about seven feet away from meeting at first. Indeed, an inscription near the Siloam end mentions the fact that workers heard each other before they met; this probably enabled them to change their course enough to correct the error.

*Early Greek and Egyptian Tunnels.*

Among the tunneling work of early Greeks, one of the best-known examples is the tunnel on the island of Samos in the Aegean Sea. This tunnel is generally believed to have been built about 687 B.C., if not earlier, and was described by the Greek historian Herodotus. For many centuries, the Samos Tunnel was lost, but it was rediscovered in 1882 through the efforts of the then governor of the island, whose workers finally unearthed the entrance and explored the inside. It was found to be nearly a mile long and averaging almost six feet square. Running through a mountain about 900 feet high, it was cut through limestone rock with hand hammers and chisels with surprisingly few irregularities though apparently it was worked from each end. Generally, the line is fairly true excepting a bend, suggesting that the headings did not meet at first. Apparently the workers in one heading were able to hear the hammers of those in the other; for one passage was turned at right angles to its original course, whence it curves back to meet the opposite heading. This tunnel was constructed for use as an aqueduct to supply the town of Samos, the water being carried in a pipe of short earthenware sections and about nine or ten inches in diameter. Workers who explored the tunnel decided that its builders started about sixteen to thirty-three feet too far west when beginning the north end of their tunnel, thus causing the failure of the headings to meet.

The Egyptians were also numbered among early builders of tunnels, and Drinker—author of one of the first authoritative works on tunneling—believed them to have been the *first* tunnel builders. This, however, does not seem to be borne out by the early historians' reports of the Babylon tunnel and the previous tunneling experience that its construction suggests. The caverns of Thebes are said to total "over fifteen leagues in length," but a league is not a definite measure of length, varying from less than two and one-half to more than four and one-half miles. Hence this leaves us rather at sea, particularly since we know that some generations used the term "league" even more freely. We do know, however, that a Theban king upon ascending to the throne, began at once to drive a tunnel which he continued until his death and which thereupon became his tomb. And one of these, the tomb of Mineptah, at Thebes, was carried for a distance of 350 feet into a hill, where a shaft was sunk and a new tunnel carried 300 feet more. This inner tunnel was then enlarged to form a chamber for the King's tomb. Tunneling was carried on in the construction of rock temples by the Nubians in the area of the Upper Nile, also by the natives of India and, to a lesser extent, by the Aztecs of Mexico. At Abu-Simbel on the Nile in Upper Egypt are the temples of Rameses II, hewn out of the solid rock, penetrating it for 150 feet and dividing into large halls and smaller ones connected by passages. A 100-foot-high façade, cut from the rock, is faced with colossi of the builder.

*The Roman Tunnels.*

We have already mentioned the Romans, and one of their outstanding works was a tunnel carrying a road through Posilipo Hill, on the highway between Naples and Ponzzuoli. This tunnel, about twenty-five feet wide by something like 3,000 feet long, was excavated through volcanic "tufa," a calcium deposit. The roof and floor converge from the portals towards the middle —apparently to aid in admitting daylight to the interior. The entrances, for this reason, are about seventy-five feet high. This tunnel is generally believed to date from the time of Augustus Caesar but authorities are not in full agreement; some place the date rather earlier. Pliny mentions a tunnel built by the Romans to drain Lake Fucino, which was apparently one of the greatest works of the time for it was three to three and one-half miles long and was driven under Mount Salvino from shafts over 400 feet deep. Forty shafts and many inclined passages were used in the work. The tunnel was evidently intended to be ten feet high and six feet wide, and about 30,000 men are reported to have been engaged for eleven years upon its construction. This was completed about A.D. 52, but, if we may credit some less reliable sources of information, its length was exceeded by the underground portions of other old Roman aqueducts which were built even earlier.

There is at least one old Roman aqueduct upon which we now have thoroughly authentic information—because it was recently reconstructed by an American firm of contractors! This is the Hadrian Aqueduct, built originally between A.D. 115 and 130 to supply the ancient city of Athens with fresh water from the underground streams of Mount Pentelikon and Mount Parnes. This early aqueduct is a tunnel which was built by the Emperor (whose name it bears) during the

Roman occupation of Greece. It served the city for many years, but during the period of Turkish occupation the population of Athens dwindled to the insignificant figure of 5,000, and the old aqueduct became forgotten. It was rediscovered in 1840—ten years after Greece became independent—and was repaired and put back into service some few years later. With the growth of the modern city, additional water supplies became necessary, and to further complicate matters, the old Hadrian tunnel had become incrusted with the water deposits of its centuries of use. In 1925 the American firm of Ulen and Company was called in to partly reconstruct the old tunnel and to connect it to an entirely new tunnel which was also to be built by the American engineers. So the old tunnel of the Romans is again serving as an essential part of the water system of modern Athens—and its water now flows through the tunnel of eighteen centuries ago which has been reconstructed and extended by engineers from the great new continent overseas, the very existence of which Emperor Hadrian had never even dreamed of.

*Catacombs of Rome.*

The use of subterranean burial caverns and tunnels was not confined to the Egyptian tombs. Indeed, the best-known work of this kind is likely to be found in the elaborate catacombs of Rome, Naples and some others of the old Roman cities. The catacombs of Rome, in particular, have always been associated with the early

11

history of Christianity, because followers of the Church were forced to make these tunnels their meeting places during times of persecution. Construction of the Roman catacombs began in the early Christian era, probably in the second century A.D. In most cases they were started as small private burial places excavated specially for this purpose by the wealthier Christians. In a few cases they were formed by the workings of old underground quarries, abandoned so far as quarrying was concerned and thereafter utilized for burial purposes. As time passed the individual Roman catacombs became Church property and were extended until the passages connected to form immense underground cities of the dead. The catacombs extending under some parts of the City of Rome and certain of the neighboring country consist of innumerable and interminable passages in which one might easily become hopelessly lost; these are lined with countless niches, believed to contain the remains of at least 6,000,000 dead.

*Chapter* **II**

# Through the Dark Ages
# to the Canals

═══════════════════════════════════════

*Ten Centuries of Stagnation.*

IN TUNNELING, as in every other constructive accomplishment, we find that history reached a complete void extending from the fall of the Roman Empire up to nearly the close of the Middle Ages. Substantially over a thousand years passed before anything of consequence was accomplished in tunneling. Even at the end of this period, several more centuries passed before anything was added to our knowledge of this art. What tunnels were built in these ten centuries of stagnation were confined to cases where secrecy of movement rather than human convenience or comfort became the prime motive. So in this age came the little narrow foot passages that medieval robber barons built to connect with their feudal castles. Even the tunnels of the great Roman Empire were allowed to fall into disuse and become buried and forgotten until rediscovered by later generations. The collapse of the Empire left a world without organization; every man lived merely for his own small circle and the only

**13**

remaining semblance of human organization was in the Church or in the feudal baron. Excepting for some few extensions of its catacombs the Church had no occasion to become interested in tunnel building, and the feudal baron confined his interest to the tiny subterranean passage leading out of his castle to provide a means of escape if it should become necessary as an alternative to surrender.

The first few scanty mentions of tunnels that followed the closing centuries of these Dark Ages began with stories of irrigation tunnels built by the Moors during their occupation of Spain. However, it was the year 1450 that marked the first substantial step towards resumption of tunneling upon the grand scale of the early Romans. For Drinker in his classic work on tunneling records this as the date of commencement of a tunnel which was to run under the Col di Tende, a 6,158-foot pass in the Maritime Alps on the road between Nice and Genoa. This tunnel was never completed. The work was dropped, subsequently resumed by Victor Amadeus III in 1782 and again abandoned in 1794, by which time about 8,200 feet of tunnel had been excavated. Later, a carriage roadway was built over the pass by Napoleon Bonaparte and the tunnel project was not revived.

### Dungeon Tunnels Unearthed in Moscow.

During construction of the Moscow subway, the workers found passages connecting with an elaborate subterranean system of tunnels which it is believed, were constructed by "Ivan the Terrible" about 1565. The discovery was entirely an accident. Russia had long since forgotten the existence of these passageways and they remained only in some old legends looked upon with scepticism by a modern generation. In 1935, the subway diggers came across some white sand below the foundations of a razed building; further excavation led to the discovery of what once had been a courtyard, with the remains of passages which had connected it with the palace of the Czars. According to the old legends, Ivan the Terrible used to witness his victims being tortured by his henchmen or being torn to pieces by savage bears in this courtyard. It was found to connect with a perfect maze of underground passages; as the Moscow press put it; "One can be lost in the fantastic subterranean city existing under Moscow." Dungeons, weapons and cemeteries were found. One of the passages extended out for some distance to what, at the time of its construction, had been a dense forest populated by wild animals. Another, paved with stone, was found which connected with storerooms and is believed to have served as a Moscovite hiding place from invaders. The discoveries threw a startling light upon conditions of these bygone ages of Czarist Russia; one finds it hard to realize that only a little over 370 years have passed since the construction of this underground maze below the streets and buildings of Moscow.

15

Just half a century before the construction of these underground passages of Ivan the Terrible, someone suggested the application of gunpowder to rock tunneling. So far as we know, nothing came of it at the time nor until many years later. Up to then, all rock tunneling had been done by hand, two methods being in use. One was the aboriginal method of drilling holes with hammers, chisels and wedges, breaking away fragments of the rock until a hole of the desired size had been laboriously cut out. The second method was a variation sometimes used with very hard rock and introduced, most likely, by the Egyptians or the Romans. This entailed heating the rock face with fire and then suddenly dashing cold water upon it to cause fracture or scaling of the surface.

*First Use of Explosives in Tunneling.*

The first use of gunpowder in subterranean excavation was made in connection with mining and took place some time around 1600; the exact date or place is not definitely known. So far as tunneling is concerned, its first use was in the construction of a tunnel for the Languedoc Canal in France in 1679–1681. This tunnel was 510 feet long, 22 feet wide and 29 feet high and was cut through tufa, a soft limestone. Whether or not it was actually the first canal tunnel is uncertain; the fact remains that it made history as the first important use of explosives in tunneling. Holes drilled in the rock were filled with explosive and fired to break

16

out the pieces. In this it unostentatiously opened the way for the great tunnels that were to follow in the next two and a half centuries. In another way also, it serves as a milestone in tunneling progress; it was the fore-runner of a wave of tunnel building that followed in connection with the construction of canals throughout Europe and which continued up to the beginning of the railroad era in 1829. At last the grip of the Dark Ages was breaking. The builders of railroads carried on from where the canal builders left off and, in the next few decades, tunnel construction was able to show more progress than it had shown in the fifteen or sixteen centuries preceding.

The wave of canal building brought with it a new requirement that builders of highways had not been called upon to face. This was the absolute necessity of a level right of way. Only to a very limited extent could grade changes be made by locks. As it was obviously impossible to run canals uphill and down-hill like roads, only two alternatives remained: to carry them around the hill or to bore right through it with a tunnel. In many cases, the first alternative was eliminated, leaving only the second. Thus came the tremendous impulse of tunnel building that began with the canals, gaining increased momentum as the rail-roads began to replace them. The Duke of Bridgewater had James Brindley construct a canal tunnel running into his Worsley Hill mine to permit shipment of coal directly from the mine workings to Manchester. This

17

canal was opened in July of 1761 and became the fore-runner of many other canal tunnels that followed in the next half century. The original tunnel was about a mile long but was enlarged from time to time, and by 1878 the system had been extended to include about 40 *miles of underground canals*. Tunnel building upon a sub-stantial scale followed this daring experiment at Worsley, and engineer Brindley figured prominently in the work. Begun in 1766 and completed in 1767, the first Harecastle Tunnel was about 8,600 feet long, 9 feet wide and 12 feet high. This tunnel was located on the Trent and Mersey, or Grand Trunk Canal, and was for many years regarded as an important engineering achievement. Some time after its completion, the original tunnel had to be abandoned, owing to settle-ment of the ground above some coal workings. To replace it, the second Harecastle Tunnel was built paral-leling the first. This tunnel, completed in 1827, was made somewhat larger, being sixteen feet high by four-teen feet wide, and was built under the direction of Thomas Telford, the Scottish stone mason who devel-oped from his original calling into one of the greatest civil engineers of history.

*The First American Tunnel.*

This wave of tunnel building in connection with the construction of canals swept across the Atlantic Ocean into the United States about the beginning of the nineteenth century. The first canal tunnel, and first

18

tunnel of any kind to be built in the United States, was the Auburn Tunnel on Schuylkill Navigation Canal at Orwigsburg Landing above Auburn, in Schuylkill County, Pennsylvania. This tunnel was begun in 1818 and opened in 1821, being cut through red shale rock. The original tunnel was 20 feet high, 18 feet wide and about 450 feet long. In 1834–1837 it was shortened to half of its original length and in 1855–1856 it was completely removed and the passageway made an open cut. So the "oldest tunnel in America" is no longer a tunnel but is now merely an open cut through a hill. As a matter of fact, this tunnel need not have been built in the first place, for it could have been avoided by locating the route of the canal slightly farther down the hill. As it immediately became a feature of public interest and served to promote curiosity about the canal, one is tempted to question the motives that inspired its construction. Almost immediately following the completion of this first American tunnel, another was built by Simeon Guilford in connection with an old Pennsylvania canal that ran from Union Waterworks along Swatara Creek to Pine Grove in the Schuylkill coal regions, a distance of about seventy-two miles. This tunnel, about a mile west of Lebanon, Pennsylvania, has often and erroneously been referred to as the first tunnel driven in America. This is true only to the extent that it is the oldest American tunnel which is still in existence. Work on the canal began between 1811 and 1822, and the tunnel was completed in 1828.

19

In its day it was regarded as an outstanding engineering achievement, and it became an important medium of transportation for shipments of lumber, grain and other commodities, until the rapid development of railroads began to steal away its traffic. In 1856 the canal was enlarged and the number of locks decreased, its capacity being also increased from that of twenty-eight-ton boats to seventy-five- or eighty-ton boats. But the continued and rapidly accelerating growth of the rails soon made this canal of little value. It was finally abandoned and much of the old bed has since been filled in. The tunnel, however, is still in existence and because of its historic associations, local citizens recently started some agitation to have it restored to safe condition and maintained as a landmark. With the aid of labor obtained from the Civil Works Administration, in 1934 they restored the canal tunnel to approximately its original appearance and placed a bronze marker giving its history. So today this early American tunnel remains as a local point of interest that is shown to sightseers who may have occasion to visit the Blue Mountain region of Pennsylvania.

*France Builds the First Railroad Tunnel.*

While the Lebanon Tunnel was being built, Brunel was struggling to complete his Thames Tunnel (described in the next chapter) and still other tunnel builders were making history elsewhere. In 1826 there was begun, near St. Etienne in France, the Terrenoir (or Black Earth) Tunnel which carried the distinction of being the first tunnel ever built for railroad purposes. The Roanne-Andrezieux line, on which this tunnel was located, was a horse railroad—having started operation before the advent of locomotives. Just a few years later, between 1831 and 1833, the Allegheny Portage Railroad Tunnel, 20 feet wide, 19 feet high and 900 feet long, was constructed through a spur of the Allegheny Mountains at Staple Bend on the Conemaugh River about four miles above Johnstown, Pennsylvania. This tunnel, which has long since been abandoned, was undoubtedly the first railroad tunnel built in America. Yet, strange to say, it was the growth of railroads that caused its abandonment! This paradox arose from the fact that it was on a portage railway and the development of through railroads took away most of the water-borne traffic that once found its way through the old Allegheny Portage Tunnel.

## Chapter III

# The First Shield Tunnels

*Tunneling under the Thames.*

WHEN the first Thames Tunnel was originally projected, around 1800, there was no thought of tunneling "shields" or similar devices in the minds of either its promoters or its engineers. This invention came later and only when difficulties of the work showed that some radical change in construction methods would be necessary if the tunnel was to be completed. A succession of Thames Tunnel projects appeared in the closing days of the eighteenth century and the beginning of the nineteenth, but the first actual work started in 1807 when Vazie (or Vesey as another source has it), its promoter, engaged one Trevethick, a miner, to begin sinking a shaft at Rotherhithe for the purpose of driving a tunnel under the river at that point. This was to be a highway tunnel, for the railroad had not yet become a factor—indeed it had barely come into existence and the steam locomotive had not been developed. Trevethick's efforts came to an end very quickly but he did get as far as to construct a small-bore advance tunnel about 5 feet high and 1,046 feet long—only 460 feet less than the tunnel that was eventually built. In the spring of 1808 the pressure of the river broke through this advance bore and flooded the whole work, putting a complete end to his efforts. In the light of our modern knowledge of underriver tunneling, it seems amazing that his work got as far as it did before this disaster took place.

### Brunel Takes a Hand.

From that year until 1825 the work remained as abandoned by Trevethick, although hope still remained in the minds of some men of the time. One of these was Sir Marc Isambard Brunel, a prominent civil engineer of the day who, in 1823, revived the project and promoted a company to carry it out by the aid of a protective device which became the predecessor of our modern tunneling "shield." This device he patented in 1818 and, although differing greatly from our present form of shield, it possessed most of its essentials and represented the first effort to provide mechanical protection for the tunnel workers. History credits Brunel with having said that his conception of shield tunneling was suggested by observation of the marine teredo or shipworm, an insect that bores its way into wood piles or the hulls of wooden ships and lines its "excavation" with a tubular shell. Brunel began work on the Thames Tunnel at the end of 1825, using a crude shield of which we shall say more later. For a time he made some progress. In May of 1827,

23

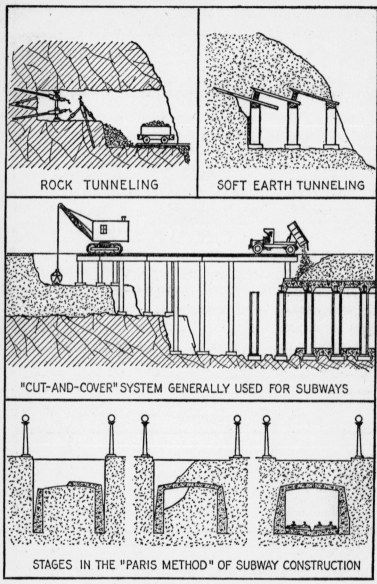

ROCK TUNNELING

SOFT EARTH TUNNELING

"CUT-AND-COVER" SYSTEM GENERALLY USED FOR SUBWAYS

STAGES IN THE "PARIS METHOD" OF SUBWAY CONSTRUCTION

Tunnel and Subway Construction Methods.

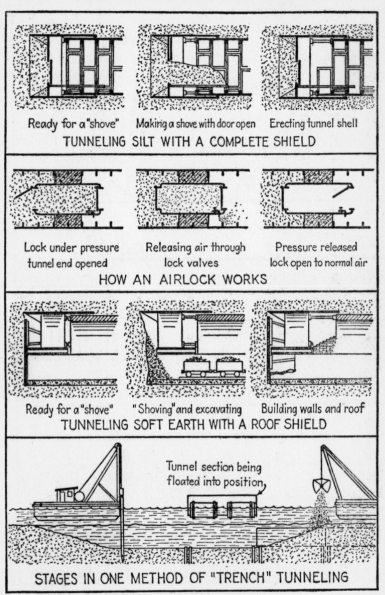

Ready for a "shove" — Making a shove with door open — Erecting tunnel shell

## TUNNELING SILT WITH A COMPLETE SHIELD

Lock under pressure tunnel end opened — Releasing air through lock valves — Pressure released lock open to normal air

## HOW AN AIRLOCK WORKS

Ready for a "shove" — "Shoving" and excavating — Building walls and roof

## TUNNELING SOFT EARTH WITH A ROOF SHIELD

Tunnel section being floated into position

## STAGES IN ONE METHOD OF "TRENCH" TUNNELING

Shield and Trench Tunneling Methods.

25

however, the river waters burst into the tunnel excavation despite the protection of his crude shield and the work came to a complete stop. After considerable difficulty, the flooded tunnel was pumped out and work resumed, only to be interrupted again in January of 1828 by another inrush of water which caused the death of six workers. This was followed later by still another accident, following which the work was again abandoned. Brunel, however, persisted in his belief that tunnels could be driven through soft wet ground, and he now directed his efforts to improvement of the crude shield.

Persuaded by his arguments, the government provided funds to resume work, and, in March of 1836, with a new shield, construction was resumed again. Even this improved shield did not solve Brunel's problems, for the river broke into his tunnel again on June 11, 1836. Again the waters were pumped out and again he resumed his fight. By this time both he and his son were practically living in the tunnel; it had become almost his sole interest. At last, however, the work went on more or less steadily until the tunnel was eventually completed in 1842. By that time the total cost of the project had reached what was—for those days and for such a short tunnel—the staggering sum of $2,350,000.

## Completed but Not Used.

What followed next is, perhaps, the strangest part of this story. With its completion after thirty-five years of struggle, one would have expected Brunel's tunnel to find an immediate use. On the contrary, no effort was made to build approaches; it was available only to pedestrians and, as a highway tunnel, could become of no service without roadways connecting it with the city streets. For twenty-three years, from 1842 to 1865, the Thames Tunnel remained completed under the river yet perfectly useless for its intended purpose in the absence of the necessary connections. It was beginning to appear as if the historic tunnel was to remain a useless monument to the folly of a great engineer. Brunel, himself, died in 1849, worn out by the fight and without the satisfaction of seeing his tunnel really put into use. In the meantime another factor had appeared in the scene. During the period covered by construction of this tunnel and the twenty-three long years following its completion, railroads had come into existence. Not only that, but they had grown from a crude experiment in transportation to a gigantic network of lines upon which the country had come to depend and which had already ousted both stage coaches and canals from their domination of the country's transport. Thus it came about that, in 1865, the Thames Tunnel was sold to the East London Railway, which built the necessary connections to carry its tracks through the old tunnel under the river. At last, a full generation after its completion, Brunel's tunnel was really put into use.

The Thames Tunnel was of such large size that, until construction of the Elm Railway Tunnel in Germany in

1913, it retained the distinction of having the largest cross-sectional area of any shield-constructed tunnel. It was built entirely of brick and without the use of compressed air, which, although suggested to Brunel by Dr. Colladon in 1828, was not used in tunneling until many years later. The Thames Tunnel really consists of two tunnels which are built as one integral construction and separated by a thick brick wall. The cross section of this structure is rectangular, about 23¼ feet high, 37½ feet wide and about 1,506 feet long between shafts. The section is formed by immense brick walls enclosing the tunnels, each 13¾ feet wide and 15¾ feet high. The top of the structure lies about 13 feet below the river bed or about 43 feet below the high-water line.

## The First Tunneling Shields.

Brunel's first conception of a tunneling shield was that of a device for dividing the face of his excavation into smaller units so that the areas of exposed surfaces might be reduced and the danger of collapse thus lessened. In his 1818 patent, he showed a circular shield or "cell" and stated his preference for cast iron to form the tunnel shell. However, in working out his device, he used a group of cast-iron rectangular frames instead of the circular shield, and brick instead of cast iron for the tunnel structure. His frames nested together to provide both a temporary roof above the heading and a means for supporting the "breasting boards" that were used to brace the soil of the working face and thus prevent its collapsing into the heading. As the excavation went on, either the whole shield or any of its component frames could be moved forward by means of screw jacks set against the finished brickwork. The shield actually used in constructing the Thames Tunnel followed this type but its disadvantages (mainly those of complication and inadequate protection for the workers) were so evident that no other shields were used in tunnel construction until 1869 when Barlow and Greathead, in London, and Beach, in New York, working independently but almost simultaneously, devised a modification which became the "father" of the modern tunneling shield. This type is cylindrical instead of rectangular, being a short tube of heavy steel plate that fits over the tunnel structure and has a staunchly-braced front end which can be either wholly or partially closed. By its use excavation can proceed by working through any or all of the openings between the heavy bracing. Any or all of these openings may be closed when necessary to prevent inflow of soft ground. This so-called "Greathead-type" shield fits over the end of the tunnel shell very much as a gigantic thimble would fit over an equally enormous finger. It is moved ahead by the pressure of jacks pushing against the previously erected portion of the tunnel shell and, when working through very soft or semiliquid material like mud or Hudson River silt, it is possible to force the shield forward with all the

29

openings closed. In this case the material is simply pushed aside just as when a pole is pushed into mud. At the extreme end of each forward movement, the tail portion of the shield still overlaps the end of the completed tunnel, thus providing a closed end within which the next ring of the tunnel shell can be erected in safety.

Coincident with his introduction of the cylindrical tunneling shield, Greathead also substituted cast-iron rings for the brickwork formerly used in constructing the tunnel shell. This was found to be such an enormous improvement that, until the recent introduction of precast concrete blocks and pressed steel, most of the shield tunnels built after the Thames Tunnel were made with iron shells. During construction of the City and South London Railway, then called the "City of London and Southwark Subway," Greathead added still another feature in the form of compressed air. This had already been used to balance the pressure of ground water in shaft excavations, having been patented by Lord Cochrane in 1830 and used extensively since; its first important use for tunneling was in the first Hudson Tunnel, of which we shall say more later. Greathead, however, used it *in connection with a shield* —a novel feature which has since come into general use because the air pressure prevents water from working its way around the shield or seeping through any exposed excavation into the tunnel. This makes it possible to tunnel through even mud.

*Barlow and Greathead's First Tube.*

For many years after the completion of this first Thames Tunnel, the enormous difficulties encountered by Brunel and the crude state of his original tunneling shield served most effectively to prevent others from attempting to duplicate his work. It was not until about 1869 that construction of the next Thames Tunnel—or, for that matter, any other soft-ground underriver tunnel—was actually begun. Even this tunnel was only the tiny "Tower Subway" with its seven-foot bore, which was promoted by Peter W. Barlow for pedestrian use, and to which we have just referred. However, the small size of his tunnel was soon to be overlooked beside the tremendous importance of certain developments attending its construction. Barlow selected James Henry Greathead as his contractor, and upon his work in building this tiny tube Greathead laid the foundation of a reputation that has gone down in history to rank him as one of the greatest tunnel builders of all time. Despite the fact that they were not the *inventors* of the shield, Barlow and Greathead have become accepted as the men who converted it from a mere idea into a practical device, thus making possible the shield tunnels of today. The first distinction of this Tower Subway was in its construction by means of a cylindrical shield; the second was in the use of cast iron in place of brick. This original Barlow and Greathead shield was a very simple affair, being moved ahead by means of hand-operated screw jacks while the

31

iron segments were both lifted into place and secured
by hand. In principle, however, it closely resembles the
improved shields of the present—the chief difference
being in the addition of mechanical devices for lifting
segments. The Tower Subway was completed in 1869
and was put into operation as a pedestrian crossing.
At first, a cable car was used to carry the passengers
under the river, hence the first Tower Subway became
also the first "tube" railway. The tube continued in
use as a pedestrian tunnel until 1894 when, upon the
opening of the Tower Bridge, it was closed to traffic and
used for the purpose of carrying water lines under the
river. In this service it remains today, still appearing
on the maps of London as the "Tower Subway," but
also marked "No Thoroughfare."

*The Beach Subway.*

While Barlow and Greathead were at work on their
famous and history-making Tower Subway in London,
an American inventor was working along remarkably
similar lines in the United States. This was Alfred E.
Beach, editor of the *Scientific American* and a man who
had long been interested in the plans for constructing a
subway under Broadway, New York. Beach's work on
this problem resulted in his forming two conclusions:
first, that steam locomotives were objectional in a
tunnel; and second, that tearing up streets for construction of a cut-and-cover subway would cause too

much interference with traffic. The outcome was his construction of a tunneling shield, a cylinder-like shell with a most remarkable resemblance to the one used by Barlow and Greathead in building the Tower Subway. Whether or not Beach actually copied many of its features from the work of his contemporaries may be open to question. At least, he deserves full credit for the honor of being the first to actually apply hydraulic jacks to a tunneling shield. For, although Brunel's patent mentioned "hydraulic presses" for propelling his shield, they were not used before the construction of this experimental subway. Beach had originally planned a subway from the Battery to Harlem. By the use of his shields it was to be constructed far below the surface, and without interrupting street traffic by tearing up the surface. To demonstrate the practicability of this plan, he constructed an experimental single-tube subway, 294 feet long, running under Broadway from the southwest corner of Warren Street to a point opposite the south side of Murray Street.

The work was begun in 1869 and finished early in 1870. In one respect this was the first subway in America. But its short length, and the fact that it was operated only for demonstration purposes, prevents New York from taking the honors away from the Boston subway that went into operation in 1898. This experimental Beach tunnel was an unlined shell of cast iron at the curves, and brick elsewhere. It was circular in section, with an inside diameter of eight feet, and the top was twenty-one feet below the street level. Its one car was propelled by air—being blown forward by pressure from behind and sucked back upon its return trip when the air force was reversed. The one-block subway "line" was opened for public inspection in February of 1870, and visitors were allowed to walk through the tube. About a year later, the air blower was installed and the car operated. For the novelty of riding under the main street of the city, a twenty-five cent admission fee was charged. Beach's subway remained one of the curiosities of the city for about two years, but his efforts to get the desired Battery-Harlem franchise met with no immediate success. So the short tube was abandoned and its end bricked up a couple of years after its completion. For years after the old tunnel remained below Broadway, completely forgotten by the public and coming into notice again only after the Rogers Peet Building (at the corner of Warren Street and Broadway) was destroyed by fire in December of 1898. Contractors excavating the site a short time later unearthed the bricked-up end of the tunnel. Once more, it was closed up and forgotten until other contractors, excavating for a section of the "B.M.T." Broadway Subway in 1912, again unearthed the old structure and found the badly corroded shield at Murray Street. This was the end of the old Beach Tube, for it had to be demolished to make way for the new subway.

# Chapter IV

# Two Historic Tunnels

*New York's Park Avenue Tunnel.*

IN CONTRAST with a very general impression, New York City's first tunnel was not the one under Park Avenue at Murray Hill. Instead, it was a tunnel considerably farther north, which was cut through solid rock when building the original New York and Harlem Railroad. This line began operation in 1837, its entire road extending only from City Hall to Fordham, a distance of about twelve and a half miles. Because the city authorities would not permit operation of steam locomotives so far south as City Hall, the lower part of this line was operated by horses. The railroad ran up what is now Fourth Avenue and Park Avenue, most of this distance being in an open cut; at Ninety-first Street, however, the two tracks passed through a hill by means of a three-block tunnel which remains in use to this day. The old reports describing this original New York tunnel refer to it as one of the sights of the metropolis and as having been constructed at the "immense cost" of $90,000. As judged by later standards, this short tunnel becomes of very minor consequence and only its early date warrants its mention. However, it became so much of a novelty that many persons used to ride on the New York and Harlem Railroad just to experience what was then the unique sensation of passing through a tunnel. With the northward growth of the city, the open-cut sections of the railroad became objectionable to residents, more particularly to those of the then exclusive "Murray Hill" section. This resulted in their bringing pressure to bear upon the city to require bridging of the open cut at cross streets and, later, the covering of its whole length from Thirty-fourth to Thirty-ninth Street, leaving only center openings for the escape of locomotive smoke. Thus it was that the "Murray Hill Tunnel," which most New Yorkers think is the city's oldest, came into existence in 1850.

Covering of the New York and Harlem Railroad cut north of Forty-second Street followed later, after which it became hard to distinguish between the covered cut and the old Park Avenue tunnel. As a result, most of the railroad's present passengers do not even know that there is an old tunnel there. For many years after the railroad terminal was removed northward to Forty-second Street, the Murray Hill Tunnel continued to be used by street cars until the advent of buses on Madison and Fourth Avenues.

*The Hoosac Tunnel—a State Scandal.*

The story of the Hoosac Tunnel began about 1819 when some enterprising individuals proposed the con-

struction of a canal from Boston to the Hudson River
to provide a more direct route from eastern Massachusetts to the Hudson, Western New York and the
Great Lakes. Blocking the course of their projected
waterway lay the Hoosac Mountain, an obstacle which
the promoters planned to overcome by the heroic
solution of tunneling right through it. Surveys for this
original tunnel project were actually made in 1825 but
nothing definite resulted, and, for a time, the scheme
dropped out of the public mind. In the meantime,
railroads were rapidly growing, their mileage increasing
by leaps and bounds. Thus, by 1848 the entire situation
had changed, both sentiment and economic factors
favoring a railroad instead of a canal. As an outcome of
this, plans were made to build a railroad, and in 1848
a charter was issued to the Troy and Greenfield Railroad Company, organized to construct a line from
Greenfield to Williamstown, passing through the Hoosac
Mountain on the way. First surveys for the railroad
tunnel began in 1850 and some construction was started
in the following year. The tunnel was to be some four
and three-quarters miles long, twenty to twenty-two
feet high and twenty-four feet wide to provide, eventually, for two tracks. Work was to be started from each
end and also from a shaft near the center.

*The State Lends a Hand.*

Because of the public advantages of this projected
tunnel, the State of Massachusetts decided to lend its

37

support to the scheme. Hence, in 1854 the State Legislature agreed to advance $2,000,000 as a loan to the company, this money to be repaid in instalments. With this substantial amount in sight, next year the company awarded a $3,500,000 contract for the construction of its tunnel. Thus began the great Hoosac Tunnel, a short distance from North Adams, on what is now the Fitchburg Division of the Boston and Maine Railroad. It became the first really large-scale tunneling enterprise on the American continent and, before its completion, established several other records also. For one, it marked the first use both of power drills and of high explosives in tunneling in this country. For another, it almost threatened to bankrupt the state which had the temerity to underwrite its construction.

The first construction contract, for some reason or other, did not produce results. So another contractor was obtained and a new agreement signed in the following year, the price being raised to $3,880,000. After some months this price was again raised, by mutual agreement, to the sum of $4,000,000. A tunnel was actually begun by this second contractor and a 16- by 16-foot hole was drilled about 600 feet into the mountain at a point which is a short distance south of the west portal of the present tunnel. The work dragged along considerably, and funds finally gave out in 1861, whereupon the state, because of its heavy investment in the project, foreclosed its mortgage on the partially completed tunnel and shortly afterwards took up the task of carrying on the work itself. Construction continued thus for a time but progress was slow and expenditures apparently were out of proportion to results. The six years that followed were marked by constant calls upon the state treasury for further appropriations to carry on the work, and soon the entire affair began to take on the aspects of a first-rate scandal. Rumors became rampant to the effect that monies intended for construction had found their way into the pockets of certain state officials. Popular feeling became resentful as these stories spread, and it reached a point demanding action. With the work only about one-third completed, the state decided to abandon its own efforts and to award a contract for the remaining three miles of tunnel. By now, the cost had already reached the total of more than $7,000,000, without allowing for interest upon the state bonds. Following this decision, the construction was turned over to a new contractor, W. and F. Shanley of Montreal, which firm agreed to complete all work for the sum of $4,594,268. Under this new contract—signed around the beginning of 1869— tunnel construction was pushed ahead with new vigor and the work soon began to show real progress.

## "The Last Agony of the Great Bore."

The final holing-through blast was fired in November of 1872, between the western heading and the portion tunneled towards it from the bottom of the central

**39**

shaft. Considerable work of enlarging still remained to be done, hence it was February of 1875 before the first train passed through. This was in the nature of a celebration. Perhaps we might be justified in assuming that many state officials made it the occasion for a deep sigh of relief. A locomotive entered the east portal hauling behind it three flat cars and one box car, the train being loaded with state officials and others connected with the promotion, financing and construction of the tunnel. The first regular passenger train followed, enroute from Boston to Troy, New York, on October 13 of the same year. The total cost of this historic tunnel has been estimated at widely varying figures, ranging generally from less than $10,000,000 to as much as $20,000,000. By the time it was completed, interest on the state's investment in the Hoosac Tunnel had become a heavy burden on its finances; a report of 1883 went so far as to claim that nearly half of the state's tax income was being swallowed up in this way. During the long-drawn-out period of its construction, the public had become considerably exercised over the charges and counter charges that followed each other in rapid succession. As years passed, with the state's expenditures steadily mounting and the tunnel still unfinished, a group of "pamphleteers" got to work. Towards the later years of the work, one publication appeared under the illuminating head of: "The Last Agony of the Great Bore"—which title may have symbolized public feeling towards the seemingly endless expenditures that were being sunk into the state's efforts to bore through Hoosac Mountain.

## First American Use of Air Drills.

From a construction viewpoint, the Hoosac Tunnel made history in many ways despite its twenty-four-year period of construction. The work was begun with hand drilling, using ordinary black powder as an explosive, and these methods continued until 1865. About this time, power drills were being developed for cutting rock, and these had already been used successfully in the Mount Cenis Tunnel, which, although started after the Hoosac, was finished before it. So, in 1866 the first cumbersome power drill was tried out in the Hoosac, and soon a more efficient compressed-air drill was adopted. The use of black powder continued some time longer, but in 1867 experiments were made with nitroglycerin. These proved highly successful and the black powder was abandoned in favor of nitroglycerin, which thus became the forerunner of dynamite and similar explosives of the type now used for rock blasting.

*Chapter* V

# Tunneling the Alps

---

*Mount Cenis Tunnel.*

SOMEWHAT earlier we made some reference to the first
attempt at tunneling the Alps, a project initiated in
1450 but never completed. It was many years later
before another tunnel was begun, although, like other
ideas of long standing, Alpine tunnel projects were
brought up from time to time. By the middle of the
nineteenth century, the development of railroads had
injected new vigor into these projects and economic
forces of international importance were brought to
bear upon them. For both France and Italy had much
to gain from a direct connection through the Alps.
Hence it came about that Cavour, the Italian Minister
of State, succeeded in bringing into line the support
of the Italian Government for a projected tunnel
under Mount Cenis. At this time the longest tunnel in
existence was the 1.8-mile Box Tunnel in Great Britain,
built between 1837 and 1841. It may well be imagined
how many doubters appeared when it was proposed to
drill nearly eight miles through Mount Cenis, more than
four times the length of the Box Tunnel. It became

thoroughly obvious that ventilation was to become a problem of first magnitude; well-informed persons believed the drillers would suffer agonies from high temperatures and lack of ventilation. A few insisted that they would suffocate before their task was more than a third completed. Engineers of the French and Italian Governments were much less pessimistic, although fully realizing the enormity of their task. Preliminary reports were convincing enough to obtain the support of both governments and also that of the Victor Emmanuel Railway Company, each contributing roughly about a third of the necessary cost. Thus the work began in 1857, with the Italian Government selected to take charge of the actual construction. No rock-drilling machinery was then available, so this part of the task began with the same old hand methods as had been used by the Romans. Indeed, the use of explosives represented almost the sole advance up to this time. The rock was sound, some of it was hard and the drillers made little progress at first. Some engineers thought it would take at least fifty years to complete.

## Necessity Is Again the Mother of Invention.

This rate of progress was not at all to the liking of Germain Sommeillier, the French engineer in charge of the project, so he undertook the development of a power drill in the hope of expediting the work. His experimental machines were first put to work in 1861 and, despite their still-crude state, soon accomplished *ten times* the work formerly possible. By the spring of 1865 the tunnel was about a third finished and on December 26, 1870, Reuter's Agency telegraphed the startling news that the Italian and French headings had met under the mountain. The dream of more than four centuries was approaching accomplishment! In June of 1871, however, the tone changed. Reports of first efforts to operate the tunnel bore news that was downright discouraging. In fact, these attempts had been distinct failures. Two out of three of the locomotive drivers had died from suffocation, and the third was revived only with difficulty. Temperatures were reported as "very high" and grave doubts were again entertained regarding the practicability of the whole project. It was beginning to look as if all of the immense cost and labor of fourteen years were to become a total loss. But the engineers had not yet given up hope. "Smoke-consuming engines" were being ordered from England in the hope that they might yet save the day and make the scheme practicable. This change in operating equipment apparently helped, for a few months later the reports told a different story. Some experimental trips had been successfully made and the great tunnel was publicly open on Sunday, September 17, 1871.

### St. Gotthard Is Next.

No sooner was this first Alpine tunnel put into operation than plans for another followed closely upon its heels. The Alps, which for centuries had remained a barrier to commerce, were now to be tunneled at another location, since the first venture had proven successful. The second tunnel was to run beneath St. Gotthard Pass leading from Lake Lucerne in Switzerland to Lake Lugano on the Swiss-Italian border. The pass, which had been in use since the sixth century, was originally just a narrow path suitable only for pack animals. Until 1820 it remained almost thus, not wider than thirteen feet at the best. Between 1820 and 1824 it was widened to eighteen feet, and its roadway was "smoothed" to allow the use of carriages, by which time its traffic was attaining substantial proportions. A tunnel twenty-six feet wide, twenty-four and a half feet high and nine and one-quarter miles long was to be drilled through the mountain to permit railway connection between Switzerland and Italy. Work began in 1872, the year following operation of the first train through the Mount Cenis Tunnel, and the rate of progress spoke eloquently of the advances made in tunneling equipment and methods. Despite its greater length and considerable trouble with incoming water, the St. Gotthard Tunnel was completed in about eight years as against the fourteen years required to bore under Mount Cenis. A contract for constructing the St. Gotthard tunnel was let to M. L. Favre on August 9, 1872; construction began at the Italian end on September 13 and at the Swiss end on October 24. Troubles with water began almost immediately. Crev-

45

ices between adjacent layers of rock showed their ability to function like pipes; jets of water under considerable pressure gushed into the workings in embarrassing quantities. Miners drilling the rock had to work amidst powerful jets discharging enormous quantities of water, the removal of which became a serious problem.

*Some Construction Troubles.*

Before this tunnel was completed, the difficulties faced by its contractors inspired some adverse comment. One publication remarked editorially that the work promised to be one of the "most expensive undertakings of the age." And water was not the only trouble that the workers had to contend with. Disease worked havoc among them because of the bad air resulting from rock dust, high temperatures, vitiation by oil lamps, the breathing of men and horses and the fumes of explosives. Deaths increased at an appalling rate. Three or four months brought sickness upon a worker and twelve months of continuous employment made him an invalid—if he was lucky enough to survive at all. Something like 200 men are believed to have been lost from sickness or accidents and as many as sixty per cent of the force were ill at one time. High temperatures added much to the troubles, ranging usually between 80 and 95 degrees and reaching as much as 106 degrees at one time. Despite these difficulties, the work continued and by February 28, 1880, the two headings were "holed through" sufficiently for a man

46

to crawl between the Swiss and Italian ends. Favre, the contractor, lost about $1,400,000 on account of his contract; in fact, he worried so much about the job that he never lived to see it finished. While directing workers at one of the bad spots he suddenly collapsed and was carried out dead. This happened at a point where faulty rock continually crushed his masonry walls as fast as his workers could build them, even crushing an inner lining placed to reinforce the first one. Before the tunnel wall was made strong enough to resist the tremendous pressure of the rock at this point, a third lining had to be put inside of the second one. At part of the Italian end water gushed out of drill holes with such force that blasters found difficulty in keeping it from forcing out their sticks of dynamite before they could be fired.

*Loop Tunnels Used to Ease Grades.*

The 9¼-mile main tunnel was practically completed in 1880, but this did not end the task of opening a route for the railway. To avoid excessively steep climbs at each end, the tunnel builders had also to cut loop tunnels through the solid rock of the mountains. Only in this way could they provide easy grades for the locomotives to climb up to the portals of the main tunnel. Three of these so-called "spiral" tunnels had to be made at the north end and four at the south end of the St. Gotthard. One of these tunnels rises 311 feet while the loop through the mountain describes about three-fourths of a circle. Just how the word "spiral" came to be applied to such tunnels has never been made quite clear; it is distinctly a misnomer. Following strictly mathematical definitions, the term "helical" would fit much better. But spiral tunnels they were called and spiral tunnels they have remained to this day, along with many others of the same kind that have since been drilled elsewhere in the world. Just prior to its opening, on June 1, 1882, the use of electricity was given consideration as motive power for operation of the St. Gotthard route. However, electric traction was still so much of an experiment that the decision made was in favor of steam. Special operating precautions were taken. A good pressure of steam was built up before entering the tunnel, and the fire was not coaled in the tunnel, thus helping greatly to decrease smoke troubles. Steam locomotives continued to haul trains through the St. Gotthard for many years, and it was not until 1924 that the tunnel was electrified by the Swiss Federal Railroads.

*The Political Aspect Appears.*

Completion of this great engineering achievement brought some results that may or may not have been fully anticipated by the adjacent countries. The most immediate result was the construction of the 6½-mile Arlberg Tunnel to provide a more direct rail route between western Austria and eastern Switzerland, a work carried out between 1880 and 1883. Of perhaps

48

FIG. 1.—London's Tower Subway under construction in 1869.

FIG. 2.—A "Greathead-type" shield at work in one of the later London tubes.
(*Photographs courtesy of London Passenger Transport Board.*)

Fig. 3.—St. Gotthard route of the Swiss Federal Railroads appears in this picture on three different levels as it winds its way in and out of loop tunnels south of the great bore.

Fig. 4.—A train of the Swiss Federal Railroads emerging from the Simplon Tunnel.

more interest, however, was the fact that this cutting
of a passage through the St. Gotthard brought about a
considerable shifting of trade. By 1886 it had become
thoroughly apparent that Italy, Switzerland and
Germany were gaining trade at the expense of France
as growing volumes of exports became diverted to the
new route. This gave rise to agitation for still another
Alpine tunnel to provide even more direct connection
between France and Italy. Consideration of routes and
possible locations resulted in selection of the Simplon
Pass under which was projected a tunnel nearly twelve
and a half miles long. This would provide a more direct
connection with Milan, the greatest distributing point
on the Italian side. The Simplon would save between
seven and eight per cent of the distance between Paris
and Milan but would entail boring a tunnel about a
third longer than the already long St. Gotthard. Work
began on November 13, 1898, under a contract calling
for completion in the almost inconceivably short time of
five and one-half years. On the Swiss end this long
tunnel would begin at the little town of Brig in the
Rhone valley; on the Italian side it would emerge near
Iselle, in the valley of Diveria. Under the direction of
engineer Brandt, who invented a new rotary hydraulic
drill for the work, unheard-of speed was attained in the
construction of this tunnel. An original plan of construction was used. Two parallel tunnels were drilled—one a
full-size single-track railroad tunnel; the other a
smaller bore. The small-bore tunnel was to facilitate

**49**

drainage and transportation during construction; at some future date it would be enlarged to form a second railroad tunnel.

## More and Hotter Water.

Brandt's drilling machines, his tunneling methods and general advances in the art of boring long tunnels resulted in such excellent progress that the Simplon was "holed through" on February 24, 1905. The first passenger train rolled through the completed tunnel on January 25, 1906, or a couple of months over seven years from the day ground was broken for the great enterprise. In the meantime, however, Brandt had died on November 22, 1899—about a year after the work began. The rapid progress attained in construction of the Simplon Tunnel might easily lead one to the very mistaken conclusion that this was conducted without difficulty. Very much to the contrary, this tunnel involved troubles exceeding those encountered in earlier Alpine tunnels. These took the form of terrific inflows of hot water, water under high pressure and excessively high temperatures that, in the fall of 1902, attained the unbearable peak of 131 degrees Fahrenheit. By this time the fight against heat had become a desperate one as the temperature continued to rise. At first water sprays had been tried, and then, as conditions got still worse, it became necessary to install a refrigerating system. At one stage the water inflow caused so much difficulty that it gave rise to grave doubts regard-

ing the possibility of completing the tunnel. In May of
1904 water coming into the north (or Swiss) heading
increased to such volume that all work at that end had
to be abandoned. This forced a change in the engineers'
method of attack; the north heading was left untouched
from this time on, the workers continuing to bore
towards it from the Italian end. Here, also, hot water
gave trouble, and, on September 6, 1904, an advance
drift of the Italian heading struck a heavy inflow of hot
water that gushed into the workings at the uncom-
fortably high temperature of 115 degrees Fahrenheit—
considerably hotter than one would desire for a hot
bath. Work had to be temporarily abandoned until a
cross drift could be cut between the small-bore tunnel
and the main tunnel, into which this water was coming
in at the rate of 2,000,000 gallons a day.

The small-bore tunnel became of immense value at
this stage, since its availability for drainage made it
possible to continue work despite the enormous volume
of water that was coming in. By this time the tunnel
was close to completion, the north and south headings
being separated by only about 800 feet of rock. This last
remaining barrier was finally cut through on February
24, 1905, connecting the north and south headings and
making it possible to drain the flooded and previously
abandoned north section. During the cutting through
of this last barrier, the heat had become so excessive
that all work had to be abandoned temporarily until
the hot rock walls had cooled enough to make conditions

51

bearable, even if still far from comfortable. It was not until the day after the first holing through that the temperature had modified enough to permit even the inspection of this connecting hole by a party of engineers. At that, two of the inspection party were overcome by the excessive heat and died later from its effects combined with those of carbon monoxide poisoning arising from the vitiated atmosphere. Considerable time had to be allowed for the tunnel to cool before enlarging the small hole to complete the connection.

## The Simplon Is Opened.

The initial passenger train passed through on January 25, 1906, and this first Simplon Tunnel was opened to regular service on June 1, 1906, being operated temporarily by steam pending completion of the electrical installation. To ensure adequate ventilation, a forced-draft plant was installed at each end and the ventilating equipment was duplicated to guard against interruption of service. Because of its great length, the tunnel aroused much interest and some doubt on the point of its ventilation. Some Londoners who were present on the first trips reported that ventilation was entirely successful; the high temperature they commented upon as being still noticeable although, by then, quite bearable. On the whole, they added, the air was considerably better than that of the steam-operated London underground.

Soon after this electrification of the tunnel was completed and the Simplon Tunnel quickly became a route of major importance. The growth of its traffic resulted in a decision, on July 19, 1912, to proceed at once with enlargement of the parallel bore to make a second railroad tunnel. The World War broke out while this was in progress, but construction was continued despite continual interruption by drafts of laborers called into the Italian army. By the end of 1921, the second Simplon Tunnel had been completed, and in the following year it was put into service.

*The Loetschberg Tunnel.*

Between the start of work upon the first Simplon Tunnel and completion of the second, several other Alpine tunnels came into existence. These included the three-and-a-half-mile Albula Tunnel, the five-and-a-third-mile Tauern Tunnel and the seven-and-a-quarter-mile Jungfrau Railway, which is nearly all in tunnel. Completion of the Simplon resulted in construction of two other tunnels: the Loetschberg, planned to give lines from northwestern Europe a connection with it, and the Mont d'Or Tunnel, built to improve its French connections. To the Loetschberg project, perhaps, belongs the doubtful honor of being the only tunnel to make such trouble for its builders that they were forced to abandon the course originally planned and to bore, within the mountain, a detour around the place where water had come in. In comparison with the length of the

53

Simplon, the Loetschberg becomes relegated to second
place. Indeed, its length of just over nine miles makes it
a fraction of a mile less than the St. Gotthard. Construction began in 1906 with no expectation of entailing any
more trouble than these earlier tunnels, all of which had
certainly given their builders ample cause for loss of
sleep. Work proceeded with no unexpected troubles
until July of 1908, when every foot of progress began to
bring in steadily increasing quantities of water. The
volume, however, was not more than could be handled
and hence was not sufficient to stop the work. But on
July 24 conditions suddenly changed. Apparently (and
without warning) the pressure of this underground
water forced out a portion of the rock. A violent inrush
followed that flooded the tunnel too quickly to permit
any chance of escape; all the men were drowned without
even a chance to fight for their lives. The tunnel was
flooded for about three-quarters of a mile from the
heading and work came to a complete stop. Investigation following the accident suggested that the water
might have come from the Kander River, a stream
flowing through the valley above the tunnel. At first,
this idea seemed preposterous, for the river was about
600 feet above. Borings were made in the Kander
Valley, however, and the engineers were surprised to
find that under the river lay a deep crevice filled with
sand extending down to the tunnel level. With the
tremendous pressure of this 600-foot "head" the river
flowed into the north heading as freely as if it had been

connected to the tunnel by a great pipe! Obviously, this called for some radical change in plans if the job was to be finished.

## A Detour inside the Mountain.

As there was no hope of completing the tunnel along its original course, the only alternative was that of changing the course to avoid the sand-filled crevice through which the river had been piped into the flooded heading. A 33-foot-thick wall was constructed in this north section at a point 4,675 feet in from the portal, the engineers saving as much as they could of the bore already constructed. A new tunnel was then started, branching off from the original bore at a point about 3,945 feet from the portal. All of the flooded equipment had to be given up as lost. Apparently, the bodies of the dead workers also had to be left in the flooded heading, the news reports indicating that there was no way of recovering them. Although the course of this new tunnel was planned to detour around the crevice until it met the south heading, the engineers were greatly concerned lest the new workers suffer a repetition of the earlier disaster. Once the faulty section had been passed, the whole staff felt tremendously relieved. A banquet was held to celebrate this occasion for, to their way of looking at it, the tunnel was as good as finished once this section had been passed. The original length of the Loetschberg Tunnel was to have been 8.6 miles but this detour inside the mountain extended the figure to 9.1 miles. Leaving the original course at an angle of about forty-two degrees, the detour carries the tunnel about 5,000 feet away from the course originally planned. In March of 1911, the tunnel was holed through and by the early part of 1913 the project had been completed and operation of trains begun.

During the construction of this tunnel, the contractors found that they had to fight avalanches outside as well as water inside the tunnel. Despite warnings of danger, an employees' restaurant was built in a certain location on the mountain side. After some heavy snowfalls, an avalanche came down upon this camp in February of 1908. Actually, it missed the restaurant itself but the terrific concussion lifted the building bodily from its foundations and threw it into the gorge below. Eleven were killed and fifteen were injured as a result. After the tunnel was completed, avalanches continued to be a threat to safe operation until the railroad took some most elaborate precautions to prevent destruction of its tracks and a possible serious accident. Terraces of earth and of stone, retaining walls and extensive planting of trees were all resorted to in efforts to prevent the start of snow slides and to divert avalanches from their course if started. This construction covered an area of about sixty acres, representing one of the most elaborate of snow-control schemes in the Alps.

In building the Mont d'Or Tunnel through the Jura Mountains, the workers again encountered serious difficulties with water. At one time, a drill, projecting through the rock into a subterranean stream, was violently hurled out of its hole, and a jet of water spurted after it for a distance of about sixty-five feet. By next morning this flow had reached the rate of 20,000 cubic feet per minute and three springs on the mountain above had run dry! At another point, the workers drilled into a large underground cavern through which waters flowed and which they explored for a few hundred feet before blocking it up. This 3.8-mile tunnel was begun in 1910 and opened to traffic in May of 1915, giving to France a new connection with the Simplon line and hence, more direct access to the famous tunnel.

## "Simplon-Orient Express."

Giving its name to one of the most palatial trains in all of Europe, the Simplon has become the best known of these Alpine tunnels. The famous "Simplon-Orient Express" provides a direct link between London, Paris, Western Europe and the Near East. By connection with the "Taurus Express" running through Asia Minor, it even serves as one link in a short route to India. Composed exclusively of sleeping cars, diner and baggage car, the Simplon-Orient has become the last word in railway comfort. Private bedrooms and shower baths represent just a few of its luxurious conveniences. In its nearly three-day trip from Calais to Istanbul (Constantinople), this train passes through six different countries—it is a train so truly international that even the time tables are printed in four languages. Crossing the border from France to Switzerland while passing under the Jura Mountains, it emerges from the Mont d'Or Tunnel and a little farther on comes to a stop at Vallorbe. Here the steam locomotive of the French line gives way to one of the powerful electrics of the Swiss Federal Railroads while passports are being examined. The picturesque scenes of mountainous Switzerland unwind swiftly as the heavy train moves again, now on its way toward Lausanne. Leaving the shores of Lake Geneva, it then winds its way through the Rhone Valley as it works upward toward Brig, at the Swiss end of the Simplon. Here it plunges into the 12¼-mile tunnel to emerge about twenty minutes later in Italy. A short distance beyond, the Swiss locomotive gives way to one of the Italian State Railways. This, in its turn, will later give way to still another as the International Sleeping Car Company's entourage speeds on its way to the extreme eastern tip of Turkey where a short ferry trip brings its passengers to the Taurus Express. A little later, they are speeding eastward towards a land that was the cradle of civilization more than 10,000 years before engineer Brandt started his work of drilling the Simplon. But the short trip under Simplon Pass is just one minor incident to the blasé travelers, interested more in the picturesque French, Swiss and Italian landscapes than in this wonder of engineering that enables them to pass through more than twelve miles of mountains in a few minutes.

## Chapter VI

# The Subway Era Begins

*London's First "Underground."*

JANUARY 10, 1863, marked the beginning of a development that was to have far-reaching effects, for on that day was opened the first section of London's original underground railway for city traffic. The history of this plan began some years before with an idea of Charles Pearson, then City Solicitor, who had proposed an extension of the Great Western, North-Western and the Great Northern Railways through a shallow subway to be built under Farringdon Street to permit transportation of passengers and freight. This original project called for what was described as an "arcade railway" of sufficient width to allow six lines of way. The plan met with favor, Parliament authorizing the construction in 1856, and by 1862 the first section of tunnel, extending from Paddington Station to Farringdon Street, was nearing completion. Within a few months, this had been finished as far as Finsbury Station, thus making it possible for incoming passengers from the north to continue right through to Southampton or Dover without the necessity of a cab ride between stations

and over the crowded city streets. Smoke-consuming
locomotives were to be used and the trains were to be
lighted by means of illuminating gas carried in collapsi-
ble bags on the roof of each car. As one additional
advantage of the scheme, it was pointed out that the
elimination of this heavy transfer traffic would greatly
relieve street congestion. Prince Napoleon, visiting
England in 1862, inspected the tunnel and advised the
Emperor to build a similar line in Paris.

This first underground was a tunnel of brick construction, seventeen feet high, twenty-eight and a half feet
wide and running only three and three-quarter miles
from Bishops Road to Farringdon Street, although it
has been greatly extended since. Experimental operation
was tried on Tuesday, January 6, and Thursday,
January 8, and on Saturday, January 10, 1863, the line
was opened for regular operation. The route was through
a single brick-arch tunnel carrying four tracks, and
each track was, at first, provided with three rails in
order that it could be used by cars and locomotives
of standard gauge as well as by the special broad-
gauge equipment that required a seven-foot rail
spacing and was constructed for operation only on the
"Metropolitan Railway." For the first six months,
the line was operated by the Great Western Railway
using the broad-gauge equipment, but cars and locomotives of standard, 4-foot 8½-inch gauge, were substituted later in the same year. In 1869, the third rails
for the broad-gauge cars were removed. In one sense,

the Metropolitan's first section of tunnel was not really London's first underground railway, for certain of the long distance roads already made their entry to the city partly in tunnels. But these were terminal lines, not used for metropolitan transportation within the city; hence they had nothing in common with the modern undergrounds or subway systems of London and other cities. Actually, the first railway to enter London by means of a tunnel dates back to 1844.

## More Undergrounds Follow.

The Metropolitan Railway was an immediate success resulting in a veritable deluge of schemes to construct similar undergrounds elsewhere in London as well as in other cities. Most of these plans died a natural death, only a few finding their way into execution. First among the successful were certain plans to construct more lines under London streets, and in 1868 the first section of the London District Railway was opened between High Street, Kensington and Gloucester Road. In the same year, the first extension of the original Metropolitan was also opened. From that time onward, additions came so fast and frequent that space prevents our reciting any more than a few of the high points in the history of the developments which blazed the way for subways all over the world. Next, in London, came the "Inner Circle" railway, making connections between the "Metropolitan" and "District" routes in 1884. This was followed at the end of 1890 by opening

**61**

of the first section of the City and South London
Railway.

## The "City and South London."

Success of the methods used in building his Tower
Subway in London encouraged Greathead to believe
that a larger railway tunnel could be built without the
tribulations that accompanied Brunel's earlier Thames
Tunnel. Thus he became interested in a plan for building
a railway line to consist of twin tunnels running a distance of about three miles beneath Clapham Road,
Kennington Road, Newington Causeway, Borough
High Street, and under the Thames at London Bridge,
to terminate at the Monument. Sir John Fowler, the
eminent civil engineer and codesigner of the great
Forth Bridge, was associated with the venture as its
consulting engineer. The project was originally promoted as the "City of London and Southwark Subway"
but at a later date it became changed to the "City
and South London Railway." Upon its completion,
this line became the initial unit of London's now-
immense system of tube railways. The first plans for
this line contemplated the use of cables for motive
power, steam being discarded as entirely unsuitable for
use in the small tubes. Detailed plans were developed
along these lines following the success of the cable-
operated street cars in some American cities. Construction began in 1886 and progressed steadily
throughout the period of the few years that the work

involved. The twin bores under the Thames were completed with a celerity that amazed the engineering world in view of the immense difficulties which had been faced by the builders of the original Thames Tunnel only about forty-four years earlier. In two short sections of the City and South London, Greathead found water-bearing ground that threatened to cause collapse of the working face of his excavation in front of the shield. To prevent this trouble he used compressed air in the tunnel, thus again making tunneling history. For the use of compressed air in combination with a shield has since become general practice in wet-ground tunneling. As *The Engineer* of June 7, 1889, put it when describing Greathead's mastery of the water-laden sand: "The system of construction made this an easy task."

With the tubes nearing completion, directors of the company began to take notice of the advantages of electric traction, which, about this time, was being perfected to the point of practicability. After careful investigation, the original cable-drive plans were scrapped and the use of electricity decided upon. Thus, when the first section went into operation in December of 1890, the City and South London Railway added to its many other distinctions that of being the first electrically-operated underground railway in the world. With the completion of this system, there followed a series of shield-tunnel projects that soon spread to many parts of the world.

*Enlarging a London "Tube."*

As time passed, the original ten-foot two-inch and ten-foot-six-inch inside diameters of the City and South London tubes were found to be too small for operation of modern cars. Hence, in 1922–1923 the tubes became the subject of a most interesting and unusual work of reconstruction. Using an open shield, designed so that trains could pass through it, the original small tunnel was enlarged to eleven feet eight and one-quarter inches inside diameter, corresponding to the "standard" size of other London tubes. As the work went on, one ring of the original cast-iron segments would be removed and the shield moved forward this distance by means of its jacks. The old segments were then reinstalled inside the rear of the shield, new pieces being added between the original ones to increase the diameter of the tunnel. The work of enlarging the tube —a job entirely without precedent in shield tunneling— was done during a few hours each day and in the early morning hours between trains. In 1900 the Central London Railway was opened between Shepherd's Bush and the Bank. During the first seven years of its existence, this line charged a uniform fare of two pence regardless of the distance traveled. At an early stage in its existence the line was dubbed the "Two-penny Tube" by the *London Daily Mail*. The name stuck, remaining long after the original two-penny fare had been abandoned. Indeed, it traveled far and wide to such an extent that many persons in distant parts came

FIG. 5.—Although its stations lack the tiled finish of modern subways, Glasgow's "Underground" is of historic interest as the second "tube" railway. (*Courtesy of Glasgow Corporation, Underground Division.*)

FIG. 6.—A four-tracked section of the Boston Subway, America's first underground line. (*Courtesy of Boston Transit Commission.*)

(*Facing page* 64)

FIG. 7.—Constructing the Budapest subway which was completed in 1896. (*Courtesy of Boston Transit Commission.*)

FIG. 8.—Two-tracked section of the first American subway, under Tremont Street, Boston. (*Courtesy of Boston Transit Commission.*)

to think of all of these London underground lines as "Tuppenny Tubes." As it is now, all of the London tube fares are graded according to the distance traveled. The first section of the Baker Street and Waterloo Railway (commonly known as the "Bakerloo") was opened in 1906. First sections of the Piccadilly route followed in the same year and the first section of the Hampstead line in 1907. Since then the various routes comprising the London "Underground" have been expanded until, by 1937, they included a total of 157 single-track miles (which might be considered as equivalent to about half the same number of route miles) in tunnels, exclusive of their many miles of surface extensions. On July 1, 1933, this entire system came under a single control along with all of London's surface lines, buses and other means of passenger transportation when these were taken over by the London Passenger Transport Board, more popularly known as "London Transport."

\* \* \* \*

*Glasgow Follows London.*

Other cities were, at first, slow to emulate London's daring experiment with underground transportation, and it was not until fifteen years after inauguration of service on the first section of London's *second* underground—the "District Railway"—that definite moves were started to create similar lines elsewhere. The first step in this direction was taken in 1883 when the North British Railway Company began construction of its

"Glasgow City and District Railway," a suburban line which included about two miles of tunnels located mainly beneath the streets of Glasgow. This route was put into operation in 1886, by which time London was already at work upon its third route: the City and South London Railway. Before the City and South London was completed, Glasgow had become the scene of another project, the Caledonian Railway Company's system of city and suburban lines including about seven and one-half miles of tunnels running beneath several of the city's heavily traveled streets. Construction of this second Glasgow underground began in 1889, and by 1896 the system was put into operation as the "Central Low Level."

Both these original Glasgow systems were constructed almost entirely by the "cut-and-cover" method and were operated by steam locomotives. To allow escape of the smoke, ventilation openings serving as "chimneys" were built upon private property at one side of the street, and, near the main station, a mechanical ventilating plant was installed. Despite these provisions, the Glasgow steam-train tunnels have always been smoke-filled to almost the point of suffocation. Passengers soon became trained to close the car windows as their train approached one of the tunnels. This move, however, served only to retard the entrance of the smoke; for in the few-mile trip (with several stops at underground stations) there was ample time for the sulphurous smoke of the soft Scotch coal to seep into the tiny compartments into which British railway carriages are divided.

## The Glasgow District Subway.

Successful operation of London's first "tube" inspired the construction of one in Glasgow, and the Scottish city soon began building its own. This became the "Glasgow District Subway," a 6½-mile loop of double tube, which went into operation on January 21, 1897—thus becoming the second tube railway. It also had the distinction of being the only underground cable railway ever built, although it has since been electrified. Much of this Glasgow tube is built at a low level, the top being as much as 155 feet below the ground, and only a few sections are less than 20 feet beneath the surface. Only about two miles of this route (four miles of tube) were constructed by means of shields, although sixteen shields were used in all. Because of the partially developed state of shield tunneling at that date, the Glasgow job was attended with considerable difficulty— perhaps even more than was encountered in construction of the City and South London bores. All but 750 feet of this London tube was built through a dense clay that was quite effective in holding back water; some parts of the Glasgow tubes were bored through a sandy soil through which the water flowed freely. In sections, the material ranged from semiliquid mud to solid rock. With the limited experience then available, the Glasgow engineers had to meet some original problems.

*"Nobody Will Ride in a Subway."*

This Glasgow subway was first proposed in 1890, to the infinite disgust of some citizens who regarded subways as a menace to health and who insisted that nobody would travel underground if he could go some other way. The fallacy of the last argument was fully exploded soon after the subway went into operation on January 21, 1897. For the company began running on the basis of a uniform fare of one penny, regardless of the distance traveled. To the surprise of everyone, including the Company itself, it soon appeared that a number of passengers liked the novelty of their underground ride enough to remain seated until they had completed two or three rounds of the entire circuit before leaving! So tickets were adopted and a scale of fares was inaugurated, which varied according to the distance traveled.

Construction of this subway began at St. Enoch Square, in the heart of the city, in March of 1891. Here the first four shields were installed, two heading towards the river, and two in the opposite direction. At one time or another eight contractors were engaged on the various sections of the line and they proved to have about the same number of different opinions on construction methods. Tunneling shields being new, some took them up with scepticism, made a few half-hearted attempts to do the work with a shield, broke it up and resorted to some older method. Others resorted to cut-and-cover methods in one form or another while still others stuck to the shield as an invaluable asset in their work. One contractor used as many as ten out of a total of sixteen shields that were used on the whole route. Another contractor went to the other extreme, building 900 feet of tunnel by aid of compressed air and lining it with iron while scorning the use of a shield. The most difficult parts, however, were built by the use of both shields and compressed air.

*Blowouts and More Blowouts.*

Two parallel tunnels driven south from St. Enoch Square to form the first passage under the Clyde, proved to be most troublesome of the entire project. The first several hundred feet were under land and work progressed without much incident; the sand was excavated a short distance ahead of the shield, this excavation lined with wood, the shield moved ahead and the iron rings erected within it. The first of the two bores passed under the river bulkhead line on September 20, 1893, whereupon the work became one series of troubles after another. Before the tunnel workers had made eighty feet of their painfully slow progress under the river, their job had accumulated the unenviable and perhaps never equalled record of ten serious blowouts—an average of one for every eight feet! The worst of these happened on February 24, 1894, when the entire timbering of the tunnel heading was blown out and up through the river, upon the surface of which it floated away, leaving a hole in the bottom about twenty-four feet

**69**

square and sixteen feet deep. After each mishap of this kind, the holes were filled with clay, the water pumped out of the tunnel and the work resumed. But, after his tenth experience, the contractor gave up in despair and abandoned the job as impossible. For this decision he could scarcely be blamed. Comparatively few shield tunnels had been built to date and the City and South London tubes were constructed almost entirely through hard clay instead of a fine sand like that underlying the Clyde—which might as well have been a wire sieve for all the help it was in keeping compressed air in the tunnel and water out of it.

## Continuous Tunneling Proves the Salvation.

Another contractor was signed up—George Talbot—a man with the courage of his convictions and who believed that the tubes could be built. Again work was resumed, but with increased care and the addition of some new precautions suggested by the earlier blowouts. Air pressure was regulated closely to balance the depth of water in accordance with the tides. As the river level went down pressure was lowered and then again raised as the tide came in. The river bottom was measured regularly and as soon as any material was found to have been washed away by tides, it was immediately replaced with clay before the low spot had time to cause trouble. Excavation was carried ahead of the shield for a distance equal to only one ring of the iron shell, the shield was moved forward and this ring installed before excavating farther. Hitherto the work had been carried on by two shifts of men in each twenty-four hours. Tunneling had remained at a standstill during meal hours; over weekends it had remained idle throughout a full thirty-four hours from Saturday afternoon until Sunday at midnight. Throwing defiance in the teeth of the staid old God-fearing Scotch Presbyterians, Talbot decided that the work must go on continuously, without stopping for meals, Saturdays, Sundays or holidays. What courage this decision required is illustrated by the fact that the Scotch, in that day and age, tabooed Sunday work and amusement as devices of the devil. Influences of the period were so powerful that the great city on the Clyde did not, as recently as 1883, permit even the operation of its street cars on a Sunday! But, from the humanitarian viewpoint, Talbot's decision undoubtedly saved the lives of many of his workers. For in the principle of continuous operation was found the salvation of shield-tunnel building in bad ground; not only are defects immediately noted and as quickly remedied, but the almost continuous movement of the shield gives them much less chance to happen in the first place. And, as a result, this first Clyde crossing of the Glasgow subway was soon completed without another serious blowout. While the first eighty feet took five months to build (and part of this had to be rebuilt), the parallel tube was pushed right through the entire 410 feet under the river in the short time of three and one-half months.

## A Fire in the Compressed Air.

Inflowing water and outflowing air were, however, not destined to be the sole troubles of shield-tunnel builders. With the advent of compressed air, a new and equally frightful enemy came into being. This was the hazard of fire, which—as Talbot knew or was soon to learn—burns with terrifying ferocity in the oxygen-laden atmosphere of the high pressure. His first experience soon occurred—during construction of the same sections of tunnels under the Clyde. Fire broke out in one of the two unfinished parallel tubes running south from St. Enoch. Fifteen workers found their only way of escape cut off and the tube rapidly filling with the suffocating smoke of burning wood. Since the fire was also between them and their source of air, the outlook became very bad indeed. Through good fortune there extended nearly to the heading a small pipe which had been used to supply compressed air for forcing lime into crevices. This supply was maintained, and, by taking their turns inhaling air from the end of this little inch-and-a-half pipe, the imprisoned men were able to remain alive for a time. Rescue threatened to become a problem without a solution, for hope would be gone long before the fire could be brought under control. There was only one chance and even that did not offer much promise; but something had to be done. So Talbot started men to work upon a heroic task— and a rescue that still remains without precedent in shield tunneling. They were to batter out one of the plates of the adjacent tube, burrow their way like moles through the five feet of water-laden sand separating this tunnel from its twin and then, in turn, batter their way into the burning tube to effect the rescue! Even the best efforts of the melodrama never conceived a more dramatic attempt at rescue. For, only the pressure of the compressed air and a few hastily placed timbers would serve as protection for the workers as they fought to smash their way through the staunch cast-iron shell of the burning tube from the cross cut through the water-laden sand between the tubes.

## Heroic Rescue Work.

The whole plan sounded rather desperate and almost hopeless from the start; but no alternative offered. So the gangs went to work in this weirdest adventure of shield-tunneling history—with the full knowledge that, at any moment, the flimsy roof of their connecting passage (held up mainly by the air pressure) might either blow up bodily or collapse upon their heads, putting a tragic end to the rescue work. Fortunately the scheme succeeded. After twenty-two hours of desperate work the passage was cut through and the despairing workers rescued. These, of course, were not the only troubles of the subway builders. In another place, the work struck an old quarry and about a quarter of a mile of partially completed tunnel was flooded before the water was brought under control. In still another place, the soil was underlain with a layer of sludge that once had formed the bed of a long-forgotten stream. This soft ooze began to flow upwards into the bottom of the tunnel, necessitating bricking up and temporary abandonment of the entire heading. The section was completed only by driving towards it from the opposite end, using compressed air and building a shell of iron segments like that of the underriver portions.

By the time that this Glasgow line had been put into operation, subways were being taken up avidly by large cities as a solution of their traffic problems. Budapest, Hungary, came next with a double-tracked cut-and-cover subway for street cars, running under Andrassy Street, one of its main thoroughfares. This line was begun in 1894, while the Glasgow subway was still under construction; because of its shorter length and lesser construction problems, it was opened in 1896, a few months before the Glasgow subway started operation. The Budapest subway was about two miles long and became the first underground street car line. It has sometimes, but in error, been referred to as the first electric subway. Such credit, of course, belongs rightfully to the City and South London Railway, which began operation several years earlier.

*Boston Subway—the First in America.*

Boston followed closely upon the heels of Budapest, in 1895 starting construction of the first short section of its present subway system. This first Boston subway consisted of a little over one and one-half miles of tunnel, mostly double-track but including some four-track line. It extends mostly under Washington, Tremont and Boylston Streets and was at first used exclusively by street cars. Most of the construction is of the cut-and-cover type, with a steel-beam-and-concrete ceiling. Some of the route has a brick-arched ceiling and one portion was built by use of a roof shield which, instead of being a complete cylinder, was merely the upper part of one. The work was completed and put into operation in September of 1898, thus becoming the first subway in America. Since that time the system has been frequently and considerably extended. Boston's subways made history in several respects. To start with, the first lines were, by a margin of a few years, the first subways in the world outside Europe. New York's original (although more extensive) subway was not opened until October of 1904. Then, the original Boston subway also represented the first successful use of a roof shield in tunneling in this country, the initial American attempt, during construction of the Baltimore Belt Railroad in 1892, having ended in a failure that necessitated the removal of the shield and resort to other methods. About the time that this first Boston subway began operating, the City of New Orleans engaged upon the construction of a series of underground canals which were put beneath some of its streets just like subways and are

75

used for carrying flood waters and for sewage. Some of
the covered waterways are twenty-two feet wide and
almost nine feet high.

## Fog as a Subway Problem?

There is one story in connection with the original
Boston subway that is worth reciting. About the time
of its completion, New York was beginning to think
in terms of subways rather than the construction of
more of its hideous and noisy elevated lines, whereupon
subway opponents seized upon the idea that, on foggy
days, the natural dampness of underground lines would
cause immensely increased trouble with fog. Indeed,
they argued, it would become so bad as to prevent the
operation of trains! The fact that the electrically
operated City and South London tubes had been in
operation since the end of 1890, the cable-driven
Glasgow subway since the beginning of 1897 and the
Boston subway since the fall of 1898 served no purpose
whatsoever in dampening the avidity with which this
group propounded its "fog-in-the-subway" idea. It
became such a bugaboo that the subway advocates
were forced, in self-defense, to means that now seem
utterly ridiculous. Boston being the nearest city in the
world with a subway in actual operation, no less an
authority than the editor of the *Engineering News*
hurried a dispatch to his correspondent in that city
asking him to report upon Boston's experiences with

fog in its new subway! This inquiry brought the reassur-
ing response that Boston had never noticed any fog in
its subway, indeed, no fog had been observed there
even on days when all shipping had been tied up by
fog in Boston Harbor! Boston, in fact, had never even
heard of the matter before.

# Chapter VII

# The Renaissance of Water Tunnels

===

*Chicago Taps the Lake.*

During the nineteenth century, water-tunnel building entered a period of renaissance involving so many cities that we can only mention a few of the American projects. Several of our lake cities found themselves in a peculiar position as their population rapidly increased. Right "at the front door" lay a great body of fresh water which might have been directly suitable for household use had it not been polluted by shipping and sewage. Chicago took the lead in solving this problem by diverting its sewage elsewhere and tunneling two miles out under Lake Michigan to an intake crib which it built far enough from shore to ensure safe drinking water. Some of these Chicago tunnels were built through a dense blue clay which underlies the city and proved to be an excellent tunneling material; later ones have been cut through the rock beneath this clay. Chicago's original brick-lined tunnel, built in 1865–1867, under the direction of Ellis S. Chesbrough and before the days of shields and compressed air, soon became regarded as an outstanding work of engineering. Cleveland followed in 1869–1874 with a tunnel which made history through the use of a small shield like the one that Beach used in building his experimental subway in New York. Chicago's first experiment was soon followed by a new seven-foot tunnel which ran out to the same crib and was finished in 1874. Others have been added from time to time, until this city now has sixty-four miles of tunnels running out to six intake cribs.

### Fire Interrupts the Work.

A frightful accident occurred during construction of one of the Chicago water tunnels. In January of 1909, about 100 men were at work on a temporary crib, 7,500 feet from shore and in deep water. Fire broke out in this wooden structure and sixty lives were lost by fire, suffocation or drowning, the contractor's tug being able to save only a few men. Some of the trapped workers ran down the shaft into the partially completed tunnel hoping, in that way, to save their lives—but their efforts were in vain, for they died of suffocation. Chicago's newer tunnels run out to cribs three miles from the lake shore, and the latest tunnel is sixteen feet in diameter. This is cut through solid limestone, which lies at some distance below the clay of the lake bed, and it was located at a level which allows at least fifty feet of rock above it.

### A Submarine River at Milwaukee.

A 3,200-foot water tunnel for Milwaukee was being cut through soapstone, sand, gravel and clay 140 feet

**79**

beneath the surface of Lake Michigan, when, on October 21, 1891, the builders ran into a most unexpected problem. Up until this time all had gone along fairly well. Then, at a point under the lake 1,640 feet from shore, some water came in through a drill hole, but the volume was slight and no attention was paid; shortly after, a blast was fired, and a heavy rush of water came into the heading. The pumps soon became unable to cope with this deluge and by the next morning both tunnel and shaft were completely filled. Larger pumps proved ineffective and the engineers were forced to arrive at an amazing conclusion when chemical analyses of the incoming water showed that it could not have come from the lake. A submarine river could furnish the only answer! After considerable trouble the difficult spot was finally passed by a detour and the tunnel was eventually completed. This, however, was not before a few years had elapsed and several unsuccessful efforts had been made.

During construction of the West Side Water Tunnel at Cleveland in 1915, canaries were used to give warning of bad air. Actually, the birds were kept in the construction office above ground, being taken into the tunnel for only half an hour each day. Despite this, complaints were made as soon as the story got around. However, the Cleveland Humane Society decided that no cruelty was being practiced and that the loss of an occasional canary was justified by the prevention of deaths among the tunnel workers.

FIG. 9.—Looking into the tunnel on Skyline Drive in Shenandoah National Park, Virginia. (*Courtesy of U.S. Bureau of Public Roads.*)

FIG. 10.—Arthur's Pass end of the Otira Tunnel during construction. This five-mile tunnel is the longest in New Zealand. Owing to the mountainous nature of the country traversed by its railroads, New Zealand has no less than 150 tunnels (aggregating 38 miles) on a main-line length of 3,335 miles. (*Courtesy of New Zealand Railways.*)

FIG. 11.—Shandaken Tunnel of the Catskill Aqueduct. (*Courtesy of New York Board of Water Supply.*)

FIG. 12.—"Holing through" Morton Street south tunnel of the Hudson Tubes, showing where the new cast-iron lining met the brick lining of Haskin's old tunnel. The brick bulkhead was constructed when Haskin abandoned his efforts. (*Courtesy of Jacobs & Davies.*)

*The "New Croton" Aqueduct.*

Among the cities which became involved in aqueduct tunneling was New York, which, about 1884, decided to build a new aqueduct from Croton Lake to Central Park Reservoir. The original aqueduct was of brick construction, built in a trench and then covered; the "New Croton" included some work of this kind but most of it was built by tunneling. Construction actually began in 1885 and on June 24, 1891, it was put into service. The entire length is slightly over thirty-three miles, of which about thirty and three-quarter miles is in brick masonry conduit, most of this being constructed by tunneling.

The most difficult part of this work was encountered on a section running through soft ground in the vicinity of Ardsley. The limestone rock, which was quite hard at first, got softer and softer as the work progressed, and, finally, a large quantity of disintegrated limestone, clay, sand and dirty water came into the heading, partly filling 125 feet of the tunnel. For fifty-nine weeks, the builders struggled continuously to carry on their work; it became a continuous cycle of timbering, clearing, excavating, tunneling and again being flooded out. Efforts were made to close the fissure by filling it from the surface but these were a complete failure and, very soon, it was found that the filled material was simply working its way into the tunnel also. This section was finally completed by changing to another method of excavation which was slower but proved more suitable to the circumstances. At another point, passing under the Harlem River, unexpected rock faults forced the engineers to revise their plans and change the course of the tunnel. Their first intention had been to drive the tunnel through rock with at least thirty feet of solid rock above it. Work was progressing according to this original plan when test holes which were drilled ahead brought in water under high pressure. As this showed that faulty rock lay directly ahead, the engineers decided to abandon the original plan and to begin all over again at a considerably lower level. The change proved to be a wise move, for the rock was sound and the tunnel was completed without further difficulty—the work proceeding without untoward event and the opposite shaft being reached in 1888.

About the time of its completion, sensational stories began to circulate regarding the construction of the aqueduct, some newspapers charging that the work was very faulty and accusing the contractors of having left great open spaces between the rock excavation and the brick lining of the tunnel. Around the same time, an investigation was conducted by the Aqueduct Commission, men being sent through the tunnel to sound its walls with hammers while listening for a hollow ring which would indicate empty spaces behind the masonry. After a little experience, some became very adept at detecting faulty portions. In a few cases, "substantial caverns" were found which had to be opened up and filled with brick and mortar. Such faults, however, existed in only a few cases whereupon the Commission decided that the work, as a whole, was not defective. Indeed, it put itself on record as stating that it saw no reason to suspect the quality of the remaining construction.

## The Catskill Aqueduct.

Before sixteen years had passed after completion of the "New Croton," increased facilities had become vitally necessary, and plans had been developed to draw upon the watershed of the Catskill Mountains. This Catskill scheme was a huge enterprise, involving an initial expenditure of more than $188,000,000, to which has since been added the $58,000,000 cost of the second "City Tunnel," built some years after completion of the original Catskill water system. At one period of construction, in August of 1911, the contractors had as many as 17,243 men actually at work along the site, without counting men engaged in factories and elsewhere on aqueduct contracts.

The whole project was so planned that construction could be carried out in two stages, to care for the city's growing needs with the passing of years. The first stage, providing for drawing upon the Esopus watershed and including enough of the aqueduct construction to carry this water to the city, was begun in 1907 and finished in 1917, including the eighteen-mile "City Tunnel Number One." The second stage, including extension of the system to divert the Schoharie Creek into the Esopus and completion of the aqueduct, was begun in 1917 and completed in 1927. The twenty-mile "City Tunnel Number Two," forming what was for the time being the final unit, was begun in 1928 and completed in 1936. In the near future, the system will be extended still further by the construction of an additional 115 miles of aqueduct tunnels to connect it with the waters of the Delaware River, the initial blast for this work having been fired on March 24, 1937. The present Catskill system includes a total of about 187 miles of which a large part is in tunnels; within the city and at some other locations these are bored through rock at very low levels. Indeed, all of the city tunnels are at such low levels that they run as far below the street as most of the great skyscrapers tower above it; each of these tunnels is large enough to pass a subway train with ample room to spare. Not all of the aqueduct construction was in tunnels, however. To keep the cost of the project as low as possible, cut-and-cover construction was utilized wherever it was warranted and practicable. About fifty-five miles of seventeen-foot to eighteen-foot concrete water tunnels were built in this way. Another fourteen miles is made up by twenty-four tunnels running through hills and mountains that blocked the way. Still another seventeen miles had to be carried through in five deep-level tunnels, which ranged from fourteen to sixteen and a half feet in diameter and from a couple of hundred feet to as much as 1,114 feet below sea level. The latter depth occurs at the point where the aqueduct passes below the Hudson River at Storm King Mountain. These low-level tunnels are called "pressure tunnels" by the water-supply engineers, because they are completely filled with water under high pressure when in use. To avoid using expensive steel linings they are placed in sound rock at such depth that the rock itself is capable of withstanding the pressure. In the deep tunnel passing under the Hudson River, this pressure amounts to 660 pounds per square inch. These deep tunnels are concrete-lined to prevent water from leaking out through crevices in the rock and to prevent ground water from coming into the tunnel when it is emptied to permit maintenance work.

### Records for Length and Depth.

The Shandaken Tunnel, forming part of the second section of this Catskill project, involved another eighteen miles of concrete-lined rock tunnel, connecting with the Schoharie watershed. This tunnel, eleven and a half feet high by ten and a quarter feet wide, was driven from each end and from seven intermediate shafts, the deepest of these being 630 feet below the surface. Exceeding City Tunnel Number One in length by fifty-one feet, it was the longest continuous tunnel in the world at the time of its construction—but it lost this distinction in 1934, when San Francisco's twenty-five-mile Coast Range Tunnel was completed. The Shandaken Tunnel was begun in November of

85

1917, and the first water was delivered through it in February of 1924. When it was holed through on May 20, 1922, the contractor and engineers made this the occasion of a celebration, a party of 150 being entertained at lunch under the mountain in the completed portion of the tunnel. The extremely low level of the Hudson River Tunnel at Storm King (1,114 feet below sea level) established a record for tunnel depth apart from those formed by galleries in mines. This job caused some editorial comment to the effect that the tunnel might never have been built had it not been for the development of electric power. For it would not have been quite practicable to operate steam pumps with the great lift and working conditions necessitated by its deep shafts. Very elaborate borings were made before the tunnel was begun, for its depth would have forced the workers to abandon construction if water had broken in. Indeed, heavy loss of life would, most likely, have resulted from such an accident. As it was, the builders found the rock to be "remarkably free" from water at this depth. In spite of very careful geological investigation, when the adjacent Moodna Tunnel was put under test some rock west of the Hudson River developed weakness and permitted leakage. As a result, the engineers had to revise their plans, changing the tunnel to a 400-foot greater depth, to by-pass the faulty rock. About 900 feet of tunnel had to be changed to this lower level, but the new location eliminated further construction troubles.

*One of the World's Longest Tunnels.*

City Tunnel Number Two, the most recent addition to the Catskill system, was planned to provide additional capacity as well as an alternate route for use in case of interrupted supply from the first tunnel. This new tunnel runs from Hill View Reservoir in Yonkers, through the Bronx and Long Island City to Brooklyn, all of the construction being at a very low level and as much as 553 feet below sea level or 766 feet below the surface. The length of this tunnel is about twenty miles, most of it being seventeen feet in diameter inside its finished concrete lining. In driving this tunnel under the Bronx River, the work was interrupted for about six months in 1931–1932 while the engineers of Patrick McGovern, the contractor, struggled to make fifty feet of progress through a section of disintegrated rock from which water came into the tunnel at a pressure of 250 pounds to the square inch. An emergency bulkhead of concrete was installed upon the first warnings of trouble—which appeared when advance borings were made in front of a heading. Considerable grouting became necessary. Perhaps we had better digress here to explain that "grout" is a mixture of either cement and water or cement, sand and water. As used in tunneling, it is poured or pumped into crevices, and since it hardens like concrete, it proves useful for stopping water. Pressures of as much as 700 pounds to the square inch were used in pumping grout to stop water from coming into this aqueduct tunnel. Painfully slow

87

progress was made here for a time, but the trouble-some section was eventually passed, thanks to the engineers' persistence, high-pressure grouting and some ingenious expedients which were resorted to. Inter-locking sheet-piling of steel, driven horizontally into place and supported by heavy ribs, was used to protect the excavation roof and sides against collapses. Despite all these troubles, the last remaining heading of this tunnel was holed through on February 23, 1932—about a year ahead of schedule. Upon its completion in 1936, the City Tunnel Number Two became the longest tunnel of the aqueduct system, exceeding the Shan-daken Tunnel by nearly two miles and the City Tunnel Number One by slightly more. Indeed, its own length is exceeded only by San Francisco's twenty-five mile Coast Range Tunnel, of which we shall say more in our story of the new Pacific Coast Aqueducts. But the Delaware Aqueduct, now under construction, will include one continuous tunnel forty-five miles long. So, even the Coast Range Tunnel record is already on its way to being broken.

## Chapter VIII

# Two Great Submarine Tunnels

*The Severn—First Long Submarine Tunnel.*

IN THE last quarter of the nineteenth century, two railroad tunnels of outstanding importance were built in England. The first of these, under the River Severn, was begun in 1873, the second, under the River Mersey, was started in 1879. Because of some construction difficulties which delayed the first, both tunnels were put into service almost at the same time. Having already fairly well covered the country with trunk lines, the British railroads had, by the seventies, turned their attention to the construction of additional bridges and tunnels to close the gaps resulting from natural barriers like rivers and bays. At this time, the River Severn and its estuary cut off the Great Western Railway's system west of Bristol and south of Gloucester from lines serving the South Wales ports. A steam ferry was being used to provide the connecting link and—in common with other roads which found themselves in similar positions elsewhere—the Great Western began to plan elimination of this break. A tunnel was decided upon in 1871, and authorization for its construction was obtained in the following year.

Construction was started in 1873 on what was then a unique project, for the Severn Tunnel would be the first long submarine railway tunnel in the world. In all, the work entailed construction of a total of nearly four and a half miles of double-track tunnel; of this, about two and a quarter miles was to run beneath the bed of the Severn. Before the work was finished, the cost was estimated at around $7,250,000, and the net gain from this heavy expenditure would be a substantial decrease in the rail distance from Cardiff to London. The material through which this tunnel had to be excavated included a great variety of substances, ranging from limestone to sand and gravel. With a two-and-a-quarter mile expanse of water above, the builders had every reason to expect some difficulty as the work got well under way. Looking back over the engineers' periodic reports that filtered through as the work progressed, one cannot help thinking that they were given no occasion for disappointment on this score. Rather surprisingly, however, the worst of their troubles with flooding resulted from encountering a land spring and the submarine portion, in general, passed through hard and sound rock. For these early days the undertaking was a large one. As many as 3,000 men were at work on the tunnel at times and 200 houses had to be constructed to house this army. By the end of 1882, bricks were being used at the rate of 26,000,000 a year in constructing the heavy masonry walls that ranged from two and a quarter to three feet

90

thick. About 76,400,000 bricks were required altogether. Explosives were being used up at the rate of 14,000 pounds per month and ventilating fans had become necessary to keep the tunnel air from becoming dangerously vitiated by the breathing of an army of men and the gases of explosions.

## Pumping 30,000,000 Gallons a Day!

By this time, the water troubles were getting under way; four of the eleven shafts were being used exclusively for pumping and three others for pumping as well as for hoisting. A total of twenty large pumps had been installed at these shafts and water was being removed at the rate of 24,000,000 gallons a day. For a time, this actually reached 30,000,000 gallons a day! Up to this time, however, the work had made reasonable progress; toward the fall of 1883, a different story could be told, for a spring of underground water was struck on the Monmouth side. The inrush forced all workers to flee for their lives, running through the tunnel to the Gloucester end without even taking time to close an iron bulkhead door which would, at least, have confined the deluge to one part of the tunnel. As it was, the elaborate pumping equipment proved entirely unable to cope with this gigantic flood and much of the tunnel was flooded. It was getting toward the end of the year before a diver sent down into the flooded tunnel was able to close this door, thus making it possible to localize the flood and pump out the rest of the finished portion. The fight to control this water went on for months, but still the bulkhead section remained flooded. With modern methods, this work might have become much simpler and ended sooner, but, in those days, the tunnel builders did not have the advantages of pressure grouting and other methods which have since been developed for stopping inflows of water. There was not much else to do but to keep on pumping out vast quantities of water for month after month in the hope of reducing the source of supply enough to bring it under control and thus permit resumption of work in the flooded section. In the meantime, construction of other portions continued while this pumping went on. In August of 1884, the water was still beyond control. Rather blandly, some news reports announced that the tunnel was now "practically completed"—except for the bulkhead part which was still flooded! The continued pumping evidently had its effect; for eventually it became possible to open up and complete this flooded portion and, by April of 1885, the tunnel was promised to be ready for operation "this year." The promise was made good when, on September 5, 1885, the Chairman of the Great Western Railway and a party of friends traveled in the first passenger train to pass through the Severn tunnel. Regular service was inaugurated on December 1, 1886. To reduce or eliminate smoke difficulties, a large ventilating fan was installed, its capacity being 240,000 cubic feet of air per minute.

*Mersey Railroad Tunnel.*

While this work was in progress at the Severn, a three-mile railway tunnel was being constructed to pass under the Mersey between Liverpool and Birkenhead. The Mersey Railway Company was incorporated in 1868, but the construction of the tunnel was not actually begun until 1880. This project differed considerably from the Severn Tunnel, the submarine portion of the Mersey one being only a little more than three-quarters of a mile long. The Mersey tunnel lies in sound red sandstone with about twenty-four feet of rock between the tunnel roof and the bed of the river. The sandstone proved to be such a good material for tunneling that progress at the rate of thirty feet a day was being reported by May of 1883. The Mersey project was most fortunate in its freedom from the serious water troubles encountered in building the Severn tunnel and work went along with considerably less occasion for loss of sleep on the part of its engineers and constructors. The headings were holed through under the river in 1884, and the tunnel completed in the following year; it was formally opened by the Prince of Wales on January 20, 1886. Here, again, as for the Severn tunnel, a powerful ventilating system was provided. In the case of the Mersey Tunnel, a separate small-bore ventilation tunnel was drilled to connect with the railroad tunnel under the river and fans were installed which had a total capacity of 600,000 cubic feet of air per minute. Many years later, this same location became the scene of another interesting tunneling project when the "Queensway," just about a city block away, was built between Liverpool and Birkenhead in 1925 to 1934. Of this recent project, which is a highway tunnel and the largest underwater tunnel in the world, we shall say more later.

# Chapter IX

# The First Hudson Tunnel

*Haskin's Tunnel Project.*

IN THE last third of the nineteenth century, Dewitt Clinton Haskin, a western railroad builder and a practical miner, arrived in New York with ambitious plans for tunneling the Hudson between New York and Jersey City. During his sixteen years of construction work, he had accumulated what was described as a "substantial fortune," all of which he gambled—and ultimately lost—on this venture. He enlisted the support of Trenor W. Park in 1873; with capital supplied partly by himself and to a larger extent by Park, he began work by sinking a shaft in Jersey City in November of 1874. Legal difficulties with property owners soon interfered and it was September of 1879 before work could be resumed. Haskin's tunnel—a substantial portion of which he actually built—consisted of two oval tubes, each formed by an outer shell of thin steel plate lined inside with about two or more feet of brickwork. Each tube was eighteen feet high and sixteen feet wide inside. A powerful ventilating system was to be installed and, as an added precaution to ensure against excess vitiation of the air, trains were to be hauled by "specially designed" engines that "consumed their own smoke." This tunnel was to be lighted by gas jets, for electricity had not yet been developed. Its two promoters believed that $10,000,000, would be sufficient to complete the project of bringing steam trains into Manhattan from New Jersey; staking at least $1,000,000 of their own resources, they began work—confident of raising the difference elsewhere.

Their optimism ran high as the work got under way, and by May of 1880 a story released for publication said: "It is expected that in three years from now trains arriving in Jersey City will run directly through to New York, and land their passengers in Broadway, somewhere near the Metropolitan Hotel, in six minutes time." Describing the construction methods, this same announcement said that "no expensive . . . Brunel shields will be required," since Haskin was going to rely solely upon the pressure of compressed air to prevent the river bed from collapsing into his tunnel while the brick lining was being built. In this respect, Haskin established a record of historic interest through being the first to apply compressed air in building a large tunnel. By a strange coincidence, he was not alone. For in the same year it was also applied by Hersent, another builder, to the construction of a very tiny cast-iron-lined tunnel located at Antwerp and having only about one-fourteenth the area of one of Haskin's tubes.

Fig. 13.—This underground maze resulted from efforts to avoid grade crossings where the Hudson Tubes branch northward and southward under the New Jersey shore. (*Courtesy of Jacobs & Davies.*)

FIG. 14.—City Tunnel Number Two of New York's Catskill Water System, where it passes under the Bronx River. (*Courtesy of New York Board of Water Supply.*)

FIG. 15.—The inside of a subway while under construction—a portion of Philadelphia's Market Street line as it appeared in August of 1906. (*Courtesy of Philadelphia Rapid Transit Company.*)

*Disasters Begin at the Outset.*

Unfortunately, however, the optimism of the builders was soon to meet with the first of a series of disasters which (combined with financial difficulties) was to finally prove the doom of their project. This first disaster came on July 21, 1880, and it cost the lives of twenty men. Work had been proceeding by means of a temporary connection between the full-size tunnel and the Jersey City shaft. The outer end of the tunnel had just begun to extend under the river so it was decided to suspend further underriver excavation until the permanent connection to the shaft could be completed. This was proceeding when air began to leak rapidly out of the tunnel at the side of the shaft, the ground there being very porous. The inside pressure dropped to such an extent that some of the roof plates became unable to support the soil above. Water and debris immediately began falling into the tunnel and before anything could be done the entire tunnel was flooded. The accident happened so quickly that there was no time to effect the rescue of more than seven workers, with the result that twenty others were drowned. In the face of this first disaster, Haskin still remained confident of success.

It was several months before the tunnel could be pumped out and the work resumed. By this time, Anderson, Haskin's construction engineer, had conceived the idea of using a "pilot tunnel" extending a short distance ahead of the main structure. This was to

97

consist of a small bore formed by a steel plate pipe just large enough to provide working space for excavation. It was to extend about ten or fifteen feet ahead of the full-size tunnel and the plates forming the preliminary shell of the main tunnel were to be braced against the tube of this "pilot" bore until the brickwork could be placed. In this way, it was hoped, the possibility of a falling roof would be eliminated. Using the Anderson method, work was again under way by January of 1881. It soon began to look as if Anderson's scheme was going to solve the problem; indeed, some years later, this plan was used very successfully in constructing much smaller sewer tunnels in Brooklyn. During 1881 fair progress was made and, by the end of the year, Haskin was able to announce the completion of 680 feet of his north tube and 525 feet of his south tube, each thus extending well out under the river. Pressure was now ranging around twenty-two pounds to the square inch and Gen. Wm. Sooy Smith was acting as Chief Engineer. By July of 1882, the north tunnel running from New Jersey was 1,100 feet out from the side of that shaft and a tunnel to meet it had just been started from a New York shaft. Even the doubters were beginning to think that all difficulties had been solved, when the press in November of 1882 suddenly reported that all workers had been laid off and that the work was again at a standstill. At this stage the New Jersey north tunnel was 1,542 feet out from the shaft, thus extending nearly a third of the way across the river. The south tunnel then ran out 570 feet, while the north tunnel from New York had reached about 74 feet. Apparently this stoppage was due to exhaustion of funds, for the reports gave no hint of any more acute engineering difficulties than had been troubling the builders right along. In April of 1883, work was resumed but progress was slow and when it was again suspended, a few months later, only about seventy-six feet more of the New York tunnel had been built.

## The Builders Run Out of Funds.

More optimistic statements emanated from the promoters who, very evidently, had exhausted the available funds but were making desperate efforts to interest other capital. By November of 1883, even the desultory construction progress was ended and the work stopped completely. It was about May of 1886 before the New Jersey tunnel was being pumped out as a preliminary to resumption of work. Now began rumors that the Pennsylvania Railroad and the New York Central Lines had promised to lend their support to Haskin's venture. Work was "actively resumed" in May of 1887 and one of the small but interesting changes recorded was in the substitution of incandescent electric light bulbs for the old arc lights that formerly had been used (together with candles) to illuminate work in the tunnel. In June work was reported as proceeding steadily. This, however, must have represented the last desperate efforts of Haskin and his associates, for in the following year all operations were again suspended with the New Jersey north tube about one-third of its way across the river.

For a time it appeared as if the Hudson Tunnel was permanently abandoned. But not for long. In March of 1888, the engineering world learned that the excavation was again being cleared out—for the seventh time since the work began nearly fifteen years earlier. A few months later, it was announced that British capital had come to the rescue and that the tunnel was to be completed under the direction of Fowler and Baker, engineers of the gigantic Forth Bridge in Scotland. Haskin still figured in the project, being reported now as superintendent of the work. December of 1889 found the New Jersey north tube 2,025 feet out and the New York heading still only about 300 feet out. Rumors began to make the rounds of engineering circles in New York, one persistently reporting that a shield was to be used to complete the tunnel. A little later in the same month it was announced that the English firm of S. Pearson and Son had been engaged as contractors for the British company and would soon take charge under a contract requiring completion of the tunnel within thirteen months. In January of 1890, Pearson confirmed the December rumors by stating that a shield of the "Greathead" type was to be used, that the tunnel was to be of cast iron instead of thin sheet steel lined with brick, and that it would be twenty feet in diameter instead of the slightly smaller oval tube begun by Haskin. This tunnel as actually built was nineteen feet six inches outside and eighteen feet two inches inside; the other tunnels forming part of the present "Hudson Tubes" are almost three feet smaller. By April parts of the new shield had arrived from Scotland and were being assembled at the end of the Haskin tunnel, 2,050 feet out from the New Jersey shaft and right under the river.

## The "McAdoo Syndicate" Appears.

Good progress was made for a time and by about the middle of 1891 the new shield had worked its way out to a point some 3,700 feet from the New Jersey shaft, with about 1,600 feet more necessary to meet the New York heading. Shortly after this, still another suspension of work was announced, "lack of funds" being given as the reason. Only $650,000 was said to be necessary now for completion of the tunnel, and the total of about $3,000,000 had been spent up to this time. Further support was not forthcoming, and in June of 1899 the tunnel company's assets were sold under foreclosure proceedings to satisfy the claims of its creditors. The partially completed work was bid in by counsel for the bondholders for $400,000, the assets (subject to some liens) consisting mainly of 4,610 feet of more or less finished tunnel and some much less tangible hopes. Optimism evidently began to sprout anew in the minds of the new owners, for by October of 1899 the tunnel was once more being pumped out—a news item

101

to which the public must have become quite accustomed by this time. This, it was stated, was for the purpose of inspection. Apparently, the bondholders had decided to see what they had sunk a couple of million dollars into!

By 1902 the situation had completely changed. It was announced that the New York and New Jersey Railway Company, backed by a group of New York business men and headed by Wm. G. McAdoo, had been formed to finish the old tunnel; that ample funds had been obtained; and that Charles M. Jacobs, engineer of the Ravenswood gas tunnel, had been appointed as Chief Engineer. Jacobs' experience with the Ravenswood tunnel had been a most eventful one, but of this we shall tell more later. Suffice, for the present, to say that it became of immense value to him in working his shields under the Hudson when completing the old Haskin tunnel. For here, as at Ravenswood, the occasion arose where his shield had to pass from soft, almost liquid, silt into solid rock. During the length of this transition he had to face the extreme difficulty of drilling and blasting rock at the bottom of the heading directly ahead of the shield while, at the same time, preventing the air from blowing out through the loose, wet, silt above—a happening which would, once more, have resulted in bringing the work to a complete stop and, perhaps, costing the lives of many workers. This particular situation was, it developed, destined to give both Jacobs and his partner, J. Vipond Davies, many a busy moment before their work was completed, but it was also to rank them as two of the foremost among shield-tunnel engineers. While the shield was making its way through the Hudson River silt toward New York, rock began to appear at the bottom of the heading. This happened about November of 1902. To prevent the poorly supported soft mass above from collapsing upon the drillers and blasters engaged upon this rock beneath, the work was suspended until precautions could be taken. A horizontal shelf was installed, extending across the full width of the shield, running out five feet in front of it, and located just below its horizontal diameter. Under the protection of this roof, the drilling and blasting began.

## Baking Silt Dry under the Hudson.

It soon became evident that the shelf alone was not sufficient protection, for the silt continued to give trouble and, as the difficulty increased, still another innovation was adopted. This was the application of intense heat to "bake" the water out of the wet silt and harden it to the stiffness of dry clay. The baking, combined with pressure of the compressed air would, it was hoped, serve the purpose of holding the silt in its place long enough to permit excavating the rock. So, for the first time in the brief history of shield tunneling, large kerosene blowpipes were brought into use and turned upon the silt in front of the shield with their powerful flames playing upon the wet material. Five of these were used, being applied for about eight hours at a time

103

while the shield structure was, in the meantime, sprayed with water to protect it from the intense heat. The whole idea seemed grotesque, but, at the end of eight hours of baking with the tunnel air pressure at thirty-eight pounds to the square inch, the silt really dried enough to be trusted. So the excavation began. Alternately baking, drilling, blasting and excavating, the shield made its painfully slow progress toward New York until it had been worked completely into solid rock and the necessity for baking of silt was removed. By June of 1903 it was announced that this north tube would be completed "early next summer" and, on March 11, 1904, this first tunnel from New Jersey to New York was actually holed through by breaking an opening from it to the short length of the old tunnel that Haskin had started from New York.

*Silt That Squirted Like Water.*

Work on the south tube was resumed in March of 1904, but the engineers' troubles were far from being over. Some time later this south shield was being jacked forward through the silt with its top door open and everything proceeding smoothly. Suddenly a column of silt shot through the open door, burying one man instantly and forcing the others to flee for their own lives. The shield in its forward progress had evidently reached a soft part of the silt. Very soon the entire tunnel, from the shield right back to the bulkhead, had become filled solidly with river-bed mud. Drastic

measures were used in efforts to "recover" the heading
—as tunnel men term the process of clearing out a
damaged tunnel and protecting it to permit resumption
of work. Two heavy yacht sails were fastened together
to make a canvas sheet measuring sixty by forty feet.
This was weighted and sunk to cover the hole in the
river bed and on top of it were dumped thousands of
bags of clay. An effort was then made to open up the
tunnel heading again. Proceeding with utmost of
caution, one of the air pipes that passed through the
concrete bulkhead was opened up—whereupon a jet of
silt shot out, almost like water, for a distance of about
forty feet! For about eight days this went on while the
tunnel workers toiled to load the mud into cars and
remove it from the tunnel, only to find that a new hole
was being created in the river bed. In fact, when the
tunnel was later cleared it was found that the canvas
itself was actually being drawn right into the open
door of the shield. More clay was dumped in the river
on top of the hole and eventually the leak stopped, the
tunnel was cleared, the body of the dead worker recovered and the work resumed. In September of 1905,
this tube also was holed through to meet the corresponding tunnel from New York.

At about this time, the entire scheme underwent
several extensive changes. The plans were revised to
include one extension of the tubes running up Sixth
Avenue to Forty-Second Street and thence to Grand
Central Station, another extension was to run across

Ninth Street to meet the subway at Astor Place, an additional pair of tubes was added to run from Hoboken to Cortlandt Street, and connections between the two pairs of tubes were included for the New Jersey side. All of these additions were incorporated with the original tubes to make the "Hudson and Manhattan Railroad." The Morton Street tubes, the outcome of Haskin's original plan, were opened for service in February of 1908 and the downtown tubes running to Cortlandt Street were opened in July of 1909. The extension under Sixth Avenue was completed as far as Thirty-third Street and was opened in November of 1910, but the plan of carrying this branch to Grand Central has never been carried out nor was the contemplated extension to Astor Place ever built. Dewitt C. Haskin, in the meantime, had long since quietly dropped out of the picture and just what became of him is somewhat of a mystery; none of those still living who were connected with the tunnel seem able to throw any light upon this point.

## Chapter X

# Two Gas Tunnels Become Adventures

*Ravenswood Tunnel.*

EARLY in the nineties, the East River Gas Company of New York (now a part of the Consolidated Edison Company) found that its plants on Manhattan were becoming unable to cope with the rapidly growing demand for gas while, at the same time, the congested area precluded construction of large new plants on this island. This left only the alternative of a tunnel under the East River so that gas could be piped from its plant in Long Island City into Manhattan. Hence a 2,516-foot tunnel, 8½ feet high and 10 feet wide, was planned to enter Manhattan at the foot of East Seventy-first Street. It was run 114 to 127 feet below mean low tide and test borings of the river bed gave every reason to believe that the tunnel would pass through good sound rock all the way. So, with this assurance and little inkling of what they were to face, the tunnel workers began sinking shafts in New York and Ravenswood in June of 1892. Tunneling out under the river from these shafts, all went well for a time, and, indeed, the two bores were nearing each other under the river when the workers encountered a section of badly disintegrated rock and soft ground that was to give them considerable trouble and nearly terminate their efforts before the work had been completed. When it became evident that the headings had reached a really bad section, compressed air was applied in the hope of keeping out the water. Work went on for a time with this aid, but the tunnel was so deep that to keep out water by air alone would have necessitated a pressure so high as to be near the limits of the workers' endurance. Hence, the best that could be done was to effect a compromise by using the highest practicable pressure in an effort to, at least, decrease the amount of incoming water. As it was, the pressure at one time reached fifty-two pounds to the square inch, the highest on record in work of this kind and a pressure which has since been prohibited by law after more was learned about the ill effects.

The high pressures soon brought serious trouble with "compressed-air sickness," which was not then as fully understood as it is today. On March 10, 1893, some of the workers who had left the tunnel became unconscious from the effects. Working shifts were reduced to four hours per day in an effort to help and thus the work went on. The job was made more complicated by the fact that the work now had to pass through a section where rock lay at the bottom of the excavation although nothing more solid than mud formed its roof. This was the first time that engineers had encountered a "mixed working face" in a subaqueous tunnel and the mud became a constant menace during removal of the rock. As a result, several serious breaks were suffered, and in one case such a direct connection was made with the river bed that even debris like old boots, tin cans and similar trash came into the tunnel along with the muck and water. After some of these experiences, the contractor threw up his hands and abandoned the job as too dangerous. Charles M. Jacobs then took charge of the work for the gas company, built a shield in the tunnel, carried the job to its final completion in 1894 and, in doing so, established a reputation which resulted later in his being selected as engineer to complete the first Hudson River tunnel that we have already described.

*Astoria-Bronx Tunnel.*

It was about sixteen years after the completion of this first gas-main tunnel before the company felt the need of and had the courage to undertake construction of another of its kind. The second tunnel was planned to run from Astoria to the Bronx, under another part of the same river. In the intervening period, tunnel builders had learned much about underwater construction; so the new job began with high hopes in 1910. But, as an added precaution, it was decided to drive this bore 250 feet below the river surface to ensure a

109

minimum of 125 feet of rock between the tunnel and the river bed. That, at least, was what their borings led the engineers to expect when the work began. The total length was to be 4,662 feet between shafts, and the tunnel was to be 18 feet high and 16¾ feet wide. The work went on with little untoward event until after the two tunnels, being driven from opposite shafts, were holed through at their upper parts, leaving only a few-hundred-foot "bench" or shelf of rock to be removed from the lower part to complete the connection. With this first connection accomplished, the engineers felt assured that the worst part of their troubles were over; indeed, they even staged a little "party" to celebrate the occasion of the holing through. Just a short time later, it turned out that the celebration had been rather premature. For, a hole drilled by workers in the Astoria heading produced a stream of water that gushed out at high pressure. More holes resulted in more incoming water and it soon became perfectly obvious that trouble aplenty lay directly ahead despite the fact that the tunnel had seemed almost on the verge of completion. Just a little later in the same day, workers in the Bronx heading began to have the same troubles with water. Bulkheads had been built in each heading and work was proceeding when water began coming in so fast that all doors had to be closed. At the Astoria side it came in so fast that the workers were forced to run for their lives before they could properly close the bulkhead doors. The pumps were unable to cope with the incoming water and, as a result, this end of the tunnel was soon flooded all of the way up to the shaft and even right up in the shaft to tide water level. Fortunately, however, the Bronx heading was saved by timely closing of all openings and this end of the tunnel remained dry.

## A Direct Connection with the River.

In the Astoria shaft the water rose and fell with the tide, proving conclusively the existence of a direct connection between the tunnel and the river. Pumping was useless; the water came in much faster than it would ever have been possible to remove it. Things looked very hopeless, but the engineers held a council of war and decided upon a new plan of attack. They would try to stop the leak at its source in the river bed. So, in October of 1913, crews were set to work on floats in the river. Holes were to be drilled in the river-bottom rock in the hope of being able to grout the leak with cement pumped into these holes from the floats. The first hole was drilled, and into it were pumped 870 bags of cement grout without affecting conditions in the least. Again plans were changed, and it was then decided to fill with grout the entire space between the Astoria and Bronx bulkheads by working from the Bronx end which was not flooded and, therefore, still accessible. The tremendous weight of water reaching up 250 feet above the tunnel created a pressure of about 108 pounds to the square inch behind the bulkhead. This caused

111

much complication in the ordinarily simple task of drilling a hole in the bulkhead and placing a two-inch pipe in it. This apparently small job took five days to complete. When it was accomplished, pumping of grout continued without interruption for forty-nine hours. During this time 8,600 bags of cement were used, and pressures up to 400 pounds to the square inch were found necessary to force the cement through the pipe against the resistance of the mud and the pressure of water above it. By the time this stage had been reached, the water in the Astoria shaft stopped rising and falling with the tide. So it was decided to try pumping out the tunnel after the cement hardened. The water was in the process of being removed when some part of the grouting gave way and again the engineers witnessed the discouraging sight of the water level rising in the shaft. Grouting was resumed at the Bronx end and another 1,700 bags of cement went into the apparently endless space behind the Bronx bulkhead. At last the leak was cut off and the Astoria end of the tunnel could be pumped dry. By November 30, 1913, it became possible for the engineers to go down this shaft and far enough into the tunnel to reach the Astoria bulkhead by means of a rowboat. Examination showed that only small leaks remained. The grout which had been pumped in from the Bronx end had not only filled the space between the bulkheads, but it had even flowed through openings in the Astoria bulkhead, running out for about 500 feet along the floor of this

112

FIG. 16.—First train of the Paris "Metro" entering Etoile Station, July, 1900.

FIG. 17.—A station on the Paris "Metro." (*Photographs courtesy of French Information Center, New York, and Compagnie du Chemin de Fer Metropolitain de Paris.*)

FIG. 18.—A "blow," or leak of air from compressed-air operations, as it appears at the surface. It was in a similar—but much greater—leak of this kind that some men were blown out of the tunnel and up to the surface as told in Chap. XIII. (*Courtesy of New York Board of Transportation.*)

FIG. 19.—Hermannplatz Station of the Berlin subway. (*Courtesy of Berliner Verkehrs Aktiengesellschaft.*)

heading. Before the tunnel was completed a total of 36,332 bags of cement had been used for grout and temporary bulkheads in the efforts to stop the leaks.

## Good Fishing in the Tunnel!

Work was resumed and, from this time on, continued with but minor incident. During the earlier stages of the big leak, however, the water had been coming in so fast that it brought with it hundreds of live fish, crabs and other evidences of the open connection with the river. The presence of the live fish proved to be too much of a temptation for some of the fish-lovers among the tunnel workers. Before this had gone on very long, they began collecting some of the incoming fish to bring home for dinner. As a current report said: "The underground fishermen often went home with a string of fish that would have shamed a surface stream." However, the grouting put an effective end to the novel sport of fishing in the tunnel, and the builders were able to finish their work, putting it into service in 1916. Shortly after this, one of the Gas Company's enterprising department heads found another use for the tunnel when he began using it as a short cut from Astoria to the Bronx while on his way home!

## Chapter XI

# Paris "Metro" and the Berlin "U-Bahn"

*The Paris Subways.*

MORE or less of an ellipse in plan, the City of Paris covers an area measuring about six and a half miles in one direction and about five and a half miles in the other. Through this there runs a network of subway lines, several of them extending entirely across the city, and, while one of them makes a circuit of the north half, another makes a circuit of the south half of the city, the two being connected by still another. All of the lines have been built and are owned by the city, being leased to the operating "Compagnie du Chemin de Fer Metropolitain de Paris." A Paris subway was first proposed as early as 1855 and in 1871 was seriously considered by the city officials, but its construction was not actually authorized until 1898, in which year the work also began. This original unit of the "Metro," as the Paris subways are popularly termed, bore more resemblance to the Boston subways

114

than to those of London or Glasgow since it closely followed the profile of the surface. The work made fairly good progress and the route was completed in its entirety and operation begun in 1900.

Slightly over one and a half miles of this original "Metro" line was constructed by the use of roof shields, a total of eleven such shields being used in all. In several cases, however, the shields were abandoned after first efforts to work them, and the construction was carried on in some other manner. Most of the route was built by a modified and quite distinctive cut-and-cover method. The street was excavated only down to the level of the tunnel roof. This roof was then built, the street replaced above it and the rest of the construction proceeded under the protection of the roof. The walls were next excavated for and constructed, the roof being supported by underpinning meanwhile. After that, the main part of the tunnel excavation was carried on, and the subway floor or "invert" was built last. The original Metro line extended from Porte Maillot on the west side of the city to Porte de Vincennes on the east side, the total length of the route being about eight miles. Later additions to the Metro's system made use of complete shields, particularly for the crossings of the Seine, of which there are now eight. Others of these Seine crossings were constructed by sinking a series of caissons or great boxes which, after sinking, were connected to form a tunnel.

115

*Where the Subway Runs through an Old Mine.*

From time to time extensions of the original Metro have been made, until, by 1920, the whole system attained a total of about sixty-two miles of double-track line. In building one of these extensions, Line Number Seven, its terminus was located near the Buttes-Chaumont Park, in a district that was formerly a source of gypsum. Underground quarries or mines that had been worked since the middle of the nineteenth century extended under much of this area, with large open spaces that were thirty to forty feet in each direction and thirty to forty feet high, the roofs being supported by pillars twenty to thirty feet in diameter— all about forty feet below the surface. Some of the galleries consisted of as many as three levels of this type, superimposed one upon the other, with roofs between that were 20 to 30 feet thick, with the lowest level extending down to 130 feet below the surface. In some cases, where the route lay through these subterranean galleries, the subway had to be constructed as a concrete tube carried upon seven-foot concrete columns running right down to a solid support on or below the floor of the lowest gallery. At one section, 1,300 feet of work had to be carried upon columns of concrete running down 120 feet.

*Berlin's Untergrundbahn.*

Berlin started construction of its first subway almost at the same time as Paris, and the initial section of its

original two-track east-and-west line was opened from
Potsdamer Platz to Zoological Garden on March 11,
1902. The subway system is called the "Untergrundbahn" or "underground road"—generally spoken of in
Berlin as the "U-Bahn." Extensions of the original line
and several wholly new lines have since been added, the
complete system now consisting of a series of routes each
originating at a side of the city and running across it
to the opposite side. This results in giving Berlin a
system of lines radiating in every direction from the
center of the city, and the five systems included now
total about thirty-nine miles of underground construction exclusive of their connected open cut and
elevated sections. Practically all Berlin is built on an
area underlaid with sand, most of it being heavily laden
with water. All the subways were built by cut-and-cover
methods, their two concrete sidewalls serving both as
retaining walls to hold back the sand and as supports
for the steel-beam-and-concrete-slab roof which carries
the street above. The wet sand gave some trouble at
times; indeed, a serious collapse resulted from this
cause when one of the more recent extensions was under
construction a few years ago. Several underwater
crossings were involved in the construction of these
lines, including those beneath the Spree and those under
the Landwehr Canal, which cuts through part of central
Berlin. The "U-Bahn" has the distinction of being the
only subway in the world providing direct service to an
important airport. Tempelhof Field, Berlin's central

117

airport, is located well within the city and one of the stations of the Tempelhof underground line, opened in 1927–1929, carries the title of "Flughafen" or "Airport." Along with Berlin's surface transport, the underground system is operated by the "B.V.G."— Berliner Verkehrs Gesellschaft—or "Berlin Transportation Company."

In addition to these lines for city transportation, Berlin recently built an entirely separate underground line, providing a connection between certain of its trunk line stations which serve as terminals of the German Railroad system. This new route forms an irregular "S" in plan, connecting the tracks running into Anhalter Station on the south with those running into Stettiner Station on the north, passing under the central part of the city on the way and having several intermediate stations en route. Since this line was put into operation, it is now possible for through passengers to pass directly through the heart of Berlin without the necessity of using either the city underground or taxicabs. Its construction involved some interesting work, particularly the crossing beneath the Landwehr Canal and the curved passage under the Spree, where the route swings out from beneath the embankment lining one side of the river to run northward beneath Artillerie Strasse. This work required the removal of a bridge over the Spree since the new underground tunnel had to pass through the foundations of the north abutment and one of the piers. The river was held back by a cofferdam (or watertight enclosure of piling) while half the subway was built "in the dry," after which this was covered over, the river was diverted to that side, a new cofferdam installed and the other half of the tunnel was then built within the new cofferdam. Where the Landwehr canal was passed under, some arrangement had to be made to permit flow of water in the canal during construction. The waterway was interrupted by means of cofferdams on each side of the subway crossing and five large pipes were used to siphon the water over the construction. Pumps were connected to the upper part of each pipe so that the water of the canal could be drawn up into them when necessary to start the siphons operating.

## Chapter XII

# Chicago's Unseen Underground

*The Unknown Freight Subways.*

UNDER the surface in Chicago, there is a subway system unseen by and unknown to many of its residents—let alone to a chance visitor. Forty feet or more below the streets of the city there is a complete network of freight tunnels that gridirons almost every part of the downtown area and has its connections running into the subbasements of most large buildings in the business district. There are no less than sixty-two miles of these tunnels now in operation; the Chicago Tunnel Company's two-foot-gauge rolling stock totals over 3,300 cars and 150 electric locomotives. The origin of these Chicago tunnels goes back to the earlier days of telephones and telegraph, for the system was originally begun to provide a means for running wires below the streets without the necessity of continually tearing up the surface every time that additions had to be made. For a time it was used in connection with the old automatic telephone system operated by an independent company. Construction was begun in 1901 under a franchise granted in February of 1899 to the Illinois

Telephone and Telegraph Company. By 1903 twenty miles of tunnels had been built, and simultaneously the funds and credit of the company were exhausted; so far as its original conception was concerned, the plan was evidently not an outstanding success. The expense of tunneling was so much greater than that of merely laying conduits under the streets that it collapsed under the dead load of its cost. To cap this, the automatic telephone system was not a financial success.

With twenty miles of tunnel already constructed it began to look as if the plan were doomed to failure and the work of tunneling came to an end for the time being. But from the ashes of this first enterprise there arose, phoenix-like, an entirely new idea that put a totally different complexion on the project. The tunnels were sold to a new concern, the Illinois Tunnel Company, and in 1903 an amended franchise was obtained, permitting the tunnels to be used for transportation of merchandise and packages. The new company found itself in possession of the original twenty miles of tunnels, but the system had no connections to existing buildings, such as would be necessary to permit its use for the new purpose of freight transportation. For a time it was beginning to look as if even the revived enterprise was doomed to failure and was to end right there with twenty miles of unused and unusable tunnels forty feet below the streets of Chicago—soon to be forgotten and perhaps rediscovered many years hence when some stupendous undertaking of the distant

121

future required an excavation running forty feet or more below the street. It took about another year before funds could be obtained to extend the system and cut through the necessary connections for loading and unloading stations in buildings along the routes. Now the project began to assume a new significance, for plans were widened to include not merely the essential connections for the existing tunnels but extension of these to link the system with railroad freight terminals, large commercial buildings and public freight-loading stations.

### A $30,000,000 *Investment.*

By 1909 the work of extension was substantially completed and operation of the system began. About $30,000,000 had been spent by the time that the rolling stock was purchased and placed in operation but the initial reception accorded to the system was most discouraging to the investors. It soon became evident that the volume of business offered was almost negligible in comparison with the heavy interest charges entailed by the tremendous cost of construction. Again came the problem of financial difficulties and a receiver was appointed by the end of 1910. Some painful reorganization followed, and in May of 1912 the tunnels, rolling stock and franchises passed into the hands of a new company and its present owner: the Chicago Tunnel Company. Since that time, the system has been in operation continuously and traffic

122

has greatly increased although the tunnels have been extended but little in mileage since 1909.

All these tunnels were built far below the streets, being cut through the dense blue clay that underlies most of Chicago. This depth is, in general, about forty feet below the surface and the construction was carried out by scooping a horse-shoe bore out of the clay with draw knives and lining the tunnel with about a foot of concrete to form walls. Air pressure of five to seven pounds per square foot was used in the tunnel during construction—more as a precaution than from actual necessity, for the hard clay showed little or no tendency to collapse while carrying both its own weight and that of the streets above during construction. The tunnels are oval in shape, being about six feet wide and seven and a half feet high, inside of their concrete walls. Each tunnel has a two-foot gauge track on which run electric locomotives closely resembling those used by contractors on large construction jobs. Crisscrossing each other under the streets of the city, the tunnels, most naturally, have many intersections—the actual figure being no less than 734. Power is transmitted to the locomotives by means of an overhead trolley and wire, and the tunnels are electrically lighted and equipped with telephone stations to facilitate the direction of operations. The branches turn under the buildings to which connections are made and end usually at the foot of an elevator shaft. Through these shafts the cars are raised in elevators to the basements, ground floors or, perhaps, some of the upper floors of the building, thus making their trip directly from the freight station or from some other building without the necessity of unloading or rehandling their contents.

## "No Other City Has a System Like This."

The whole system is essentially a railroad and is operated like one. Signals protect the trainmen when picking up, delivering or switching cars and some sections are even equipped with an automatic block system. A centrally located train dispatcher controls all train movements by means of some 300 telephones distributed at strategic points throughout the system and the operating company boasts that there has never been a serious accident in these tunnels—a record that many operators of motor trucks no doubt wish they could equal. As the present operators tackled the problem of developing business for the tunnels, new uses came to light, and today they are not confined to freight handling, although this still remains the main purpose. Many large buildings now receive their coal supplies and dispose of their ashes through the tunnels. But one of the most novel uses of this tunnel system is made when a building is being demolished or a new one constructed. When the size of the job warrants, a connection is cut from the excavation into a branch of the tunnel system and, through this, all of the refuse is carried away from the site in tunnel cars. All that one sees is merely a hole about the size of a sewer manhole;

into this the workers shovel all their debris, and, so far as they are concerned, that is the end of it. Down through the chute it goes, directly into tunnel cars specially assigned to this use. Through the tunnels it is hauled to some portion of the system where filling is in progress. Hundreds of acres of Chicago's great lake-front parks have been filled in this manner.

So, unseen and unheard by those on the surface or in the business floors of the buildings, the Chicago Tunnel Company's 150 locomotives rumble through the deep tunnels, just a little higher than enough to provide comfortable headroom for a tall man, trailing behind them long trains of small cars loaded with merchandise in transit from warehouses to department stores; with coal on its way to some large Loop building or, perhaps, ashes or the debris from some excavation on its way to a point where more lake-front filling is in progress. It is indeed, a unique system, and the Chicago Tunnel Company has unquestioned ground for its proud boast that "no other city in the world has a freight system like this!"

## Chapter XIII

# New York and Philadelphia Subways

===========

*The World's Biggest Subway Network.*

FOR several decades now, the City of New York has been a center of tunneling activity. By 1937 there were nine individual tubes running under the Hudson River with one more in process of construction; under the Harlem River were seven tubes, while the East River had no less than twenty-six tubes with still two more under construction. These figures, of course, count as two individual tubes all double-tube tunnels and they include not only the rapid transit tunnels but also the railroad, highway, large gas tunnels and deep-level aqueducts. Much of the city itself is similarly honeycombed with subways and tunnels. Four distinctly separate rapid transit systems enter Manhattan underground: the Interborough Rapid Transit system, the Brooklyn-Manhattan Transit system, the Hudson and Manhattan Railroad and the city-operated "Independent" or Eighth Avenue Subway system. Between all of them, these systems include a total of about 136 route miles of *underground* lines in New York City and adjacent cities on the New Jersey side. At some points in Manhattan we find as many as five parallel subways with anywhere from a few feet to a couple of blocks separating them; at many places they are two and three layers deep. With so much underground, it has become quite common to hear the joking remark that "Some day this town will fall into the tunnels." Of which, however, the reader may rest fully assured there is no danger. For the solidly built steel-and-concrete subways and tunnels are fully capable of carrying their intended loads with a tremendous margin of safety.

The history of this gigantic system really began with the old Beach Tunnel of 1869–1870. Despite the fact that nothing further was accomplished for many years after, the subway project kept bobbing up with almost constant regularity. It was retarded by the fact that New York, in a misguided moment, decided first in favor of elevated railroads—a decision that subsequent generations have since had ample cause to regret and plenty of time in which to do it. The Beach franchise for a Broadway subway found its way into other hands as the years passed, and the records refer to a whole series of proposals covering a long span of years. But, despite the number of these projects, nothing tangible was attained by New York from the construction of Beach's experimental subway tunnel in 1869 until the city itself took up the problem some years later. The delay can be charged mainly to financing difficulties, for no banker could be found who believed that people would ride in a subway! In 1899, however, the city succeeded in working out a plan of financing. From that time onwards, action was "fast and furious." On a memorable day, February 21, 1900, the city awarded its first contract for the initial section of its first subway. Work began immediately, ground being broken formally when Mayor Robert A. Van Wyck dug the first shovelful of earth in front of the City Hall on March 24 of the same year.

## The City's First Subway Is Begun.

Two days later, contractor John B. McDonald went to work in earnest, and within a short time the city was entering its first throes of subway building; busy streets were torn up and their paving replaced with temporary planking, under the cover of which the work of excavation and construction went on. The subway started on its way by Van Wyck's shovelful of earth was only a small part of the present system and, as a matter of fact, did not even constitute the whole of the original system. It was to run only from City Hall to Dyckman Street, with a branch extending eastward from a point above Ninety-sixth Street through Harlem to the Bronx. By the beginnning of 1901, the Rapid Transit Commission had already approved an extension of this line down Broadway and under the East River to Brooklyn. The rapidity of expansion brought some interesting side lights in itself, such as in the case of a

FIG. 20.—Starting excavation for the Sixth Avenue Subway in New York. (*Courtesy of New York Board of Transportation.*)

FIG. 21.—A train in one of the Philadelphia subways. (*Courtesy of Philadelphia Rapid Transit Company.*)

Fig. 22.—Interior of the Rove Canal Tunnel in France, the world's largest tunnel in volume of excavation and second largest in cross-sectional area. (*Photograph by Jacques Boyer.*)

Fig. 23.—"Holing through" Tunnel Number One at Parker Dam on the Colorado River. (*Courtesy of U.S. Bureau of Reclamation.*)

section under Broadway between 135th and 138th Streets. Here the original plans had called for a two-tracked line, and this part was built before it could be realized that a third track had become desirable. Toward the end of 1901, the contractor was ordered to widen the already completed tunnel for a third track, and, to save the destruction of completed work, he resorted to a most original method. Instead of tearing down the new tunnel, he performed a "surgical operation" on it. Splitting it down the middle, he moved each piece bodily five-and-a-half feet to one side into a space excavated to receive it! New columns were installed and upon these he built a roof across the space between his two strips of tunnel, this whole reconstruction extending for a distance of about three city blocks.

*Harlem River Tunnels.*

Where the Bronx extension of this subway passed under the Harlem River a novel method of construction was used. The underriver section here was about 610 feet long, of which some 400 feet lay between the pierheads lining the river. Because of its short length and other conditions, a variation of the "trench system" of construction was chosen as being more economical than the use of shields. The first step was to dredge a trench in the river bed, the bottom of this trench being carried down to a level that would permit construction of the upper half of the tunnel. Piling was then driven into the river bed on each side of the trench along the line of the tunnel and this was cut off under water to provide a support for the upper portion of the tunnel. The Manhattan half was constructed first and the Bronx half later, two different methods being used because the contractor was not thoroughly satisfied with the first method. In constructing this first half, a wooden box was sunk until it rested upon the piling which had been cut off under water. Above this box backfill was dumped to restore the river bed to its original level and, with the protection of this roof, the excavation was completed and the cast-iron shell was set in position, compressed air being used meanwhile to keep the water out. When building the second half, no box was used, the tunnel roof sections themselves providing a roof during construction. These Harlem River subway tubes are "Siamese twins." Instead of being separate, they are connected together so that only a wall of iron separates one from the other while outside this iron shell is a protective casing of concrete.

The first tunnels under the East River, forming part of the Brooklyn extension of this original subway, were begun on March 24, 1903, with the start of a shaft at Joralemon Street, Brooklyn. Two separate tubes were built, each with a cast iron shell almost 17 feet outside and about 6,766 feet long, two-thirds of this construction requiring the use of tunneling shields. Having the advantage of New York's experience in tunneling under the Hudson this was not so much of an original engineering experience as that of building the tubes to New Jersey. Nevertheless, it was far from being uneventful—as the contractors and engineers soon found when they began to accumulate experience with "blows" and flooding. In one of these, a certain "sandhog" had an escape that has been repeated only once since, and, rather strange to say, the second incident happened during the construction of a nearby tunnel which was built some years later for one of the more recent subways.

*Workman Blown Out of the Tunnel into the River.*

The first event occurred on March 27, 1905. The Brooklyn shield used in driving the first of these East River tunnels was about 200 feet out from the shaft and 75 feet beyond the river bulkhead; only five feet of river bed mud lay between it and the fifteen feet of menacing water above. Eight men were at work under the direction of Richard Creegan, who was described in the reports as "an expert tunnelman." Just as the gang started work, a leak began to develop in the unstable mud roof in front of the shield. Creegan made an attempt to close it with the bags of hay that were kept on hand for such contingencies, and he succeeded in getting the first bag into place. Just as he pushed a second into the soft spot through which the air had been escaping, there came a sudden upward rush of air blowing its way through the mud toward the river.

131

Caught momentarily off his guard, Creegan was swept from his feet and upward into the river mud above. His companions witnessed the harrowing sight of his whole body being sucked into the mud. For a moment he remained there, buried alive in the river bed with only his feet showing in the heading below. But it was only for a moment. Before the others could make any move to help him, the feet also disappeared from their view as another rush of air carried him bodily upward. Through the five feet of mud and the fifteen feet of water he was hurled by the force of escaping air, and he shot to the surface, where he was quickly rescued by some amazed longshoremen. To the surprise of everyone, and particularly that of his companions, he soon proved to be none the worse of his unusual experience.

*An East River Tube Carried on Stilts.*

Even the virtual completion of these first East River Tubes did not terminate the engineers' troubles. For, as the tunnel construction progressed, it became apparent that some of the completed sections were slowly sinking in the unstable bed. Indeed, this had reached a stage where the round tube became flattened to something approaching the shape of an egg. The deformation became so great that trains would have scraped on the sides of the tunnel had it been put into service, whereupon the engineers had no choice but to reconstruct this portion. Accordingly, the bottom plates were taken out during 1906 and were replaced by others which restored, more or less, the intended shape of the tube. A total of about 2,500 feet of tunnel was rebuilt in this manner. A little later, the engineers decided to take precautions against more trouble arising from the same source. Hence, in 1907, twenty pile foundations were sunk ten to fifty feet down to bedrock so that the finished tunnels are now carried by the rock which lies below. This innovation established a precedent in tunnel building, being the first time that a shield tunnel had to be carried on stilts. The method proved to be most successful, for it put an end to the sinking troubles and the first train was operated through the tube on November 27, 1907. Regular service began on January 9, 1908.

## A Job That Is Never Ended.

The original system was completed sufficiently to get the first sections (from Brooklyn Bridge to 145th Street and Broadway) into operation on October 27, 1904, and, on that day, the city's first subway trains began operating. Less than nine months later, the extensions to South Ferry and to the Bronx were added; the Brooklyn extension went into operation as far as Borough Hall early in 1908 and later was opened through to Atlantic Avenue. To the older residents of New York, it has always seemed as though this first subway was barely finished before the need of still others became pressing. Indeed, before the original system went into operation in its entirety, another and

133

independent project had already been started which, at a later date, became incorporated as a part of the extended system. This was the pair of "Steinway Tunnels" running from East Forty-second Street, Manhattan, to Long Island City and upon which work began in earnest about 1905. These tunnels (which have also been called the "Belmont Tunnels" from association of August Belmont with their financing) were constructed under an old franchise, the terms apparently causing some question about possible lapse of rights. Originally begun in May of 1892, the work was suspended in December of the same year. For thirteen years it remained abandoned until resumed in 1905, when the rights were acquired by the Interborough Rapid Transit Company and, by September 23, 1907, the first car was operated through the north tube of the pair. By the next year both tubes were virtually complete. About this time, the company was making efforts to sell these tunnels outright to the city, the property being limited to the pair of tubes "dead-ended" under East Forty-second Street at Lexington Avenue, since the old franchise did not provide for any Manhattan connections. The city, however, took the position that the company's legal rights under its franchise had expired before the tunnels were ready and, upon these grounds, the Public Service Commission, in 1909, refused to consider their purchase at any price. Following this deadlock, the tubes remained practically complete yet idle until 1915. In the meantime, they had been acquired by the city as part of a general agreement with the Interborough Rapid Transit Company, and they were made a part of the "dual-system" subway plans when these were agreed upon in 1913. Regular operation of these tunnels began with a shuttle-car service on June 22, 1915, and a few years later they were connected with the new elevated extensions in Queens and through subway trains were operated. In March of 1927, they were extended across to Seventh Avenue and West Forty-first Street, making connections there for exchange of passengers with the new West Side Subway of the Interborough system.

### The "Dual-System" Agreements.

The so-called "dual system" was the outcome of a seemingly endless wrangle over the question of who should build and who should operate new subways and how they should tie in with existing lines. An agreement was signed on March 19, 1913, by the New York Municipal Railway Company (affiliated with the Brooklyn Rapid Transit Company), the Interborough Rapid Transit Company and the Public Service Commission of the City of New York. Construction began soon after, the new routes consisting of new lines and extensions of old lines of both the Interborough and Brooklyn systems. These included subway extensions of the "B.R.T." into Manhattan and subway extensions of the "I.R.T." farther into Brooklyn, in addition to many elevated lines. In connection with its entry into

135

Manhattan, the Brooklyn Rapid Transit Company became the Brooklyn-Manhattan Transit Company; its "Broadway" subway came into existence under these agreements and likewise came the Interborough's West Side line south of Forty-second Street and its East Side line north of the same street. In the shuffling around which took place in connection with this rearrangement, the Forty-second Street portion of New York's original subway was discontinued as a through route, and it has since served as a cross-town "shuttle" between Grand Central Station and Times Square. The dual-system plans included a second pair of I.R.T. tunnels and a pair of B.M.T. tunnels under the East River in the downtown district of Manhattan. It also included the pair of B.M.T. tunnels under the East River to Queens at East Sixtieth Street. A little later, still another section was added to the B.M.T. system, the "Fourteenth Street Eastern Line," consisting of a subway under Fourteenth Street, Manhattan, passing under the East River and the northern sections of Brooklyn to meet existing elevated lines at East New York.

During construction of the new I.R.T. tubes under the East River, another incident occurred like the one that happened to Creegan when the original subway tunnel, a few blocks to the south of this new crossing, was under construction. A blowout started in one of the headings at about 4 P.M. on February 19, 1916, just as the sandhogs were preparing to jack the shield

136

forward in another "shove." Here again a hole appeared
in the mud roof and air began to escape. One man tried
to plug the hole with a bag of sand but he was instantly
drawn up into the river. Almost immediately after him
two others were sucked up before they could escape to
safety through the shield in front of which they were
working. Water, of course, rushed in through the opening and flooded the tunnel. In this accident, however,
the principals were not as fortunate as Creegan; only
one of them—Marshall Mabey—survived.

## The "Independent" Subway.

Even before these great extensions of the New York
subways were put into actual operation, the City had
begun to feel the need of still other additions to its
rapidly growing transportation system. Hence, in 1925
there was adopted a plan for a third system to be constructed as a unit entirely separate from the two
networks already in operation. This is called the
"Independent" system but is popularly known as the
"Eighth Avenue Subway." It comprises about fifty-
three miles of subway routes in Manhattan, Bronx,
Brooklyn and Queens without including the new Sixth
Avenue line which is being built. Although having no
direct rail connections with the older systems, passageways have been provided at some transfer points
and the new system has been so planned that actual rail
connections can be made at certain points in future.
The first unit, running from Fulton Street to 207th

Street, went into operation on September 10, 1932, with the city itself conducting the operation through its Board of Transportation. Since that time, one section after another has been opened until the system is now almost completed, the Jamaica unit having started operation in April of 1937. A last link, running under Sixth Avenue from Eighth Street to Fifty-third Street, New York, is under construction.

Both the B.M.T. pair of tubes running under the East River at Sixtieth Street and the pair of Eighth Avenue Subway tubes running under the same river at Fifty-third Street have one peculiar feature that they share in common. This arose from the fact that the west channel of the East River is very deep, making it impracticable to carry the tunnels below its normal bed. Hence a depth was chosen which would have carried the tubes above the bed and right through the water had nothing been done about it. Before construction began, however, the bed was artificially raised at the points of crossing. Clay was dumped from scows and this was followed by riprap or large broken stone to keep the clay in place. Through this artificially formed bed, the tubes were then built by shields in the usual manner. Thus passengers using these tunnels of the two subways have—even though they seldom know it—the unique experience of riding *through* the East River instead of under its bed!

Many of the more recent of these New York subways had to be constructed under conditions that caused tremendous complication for the contractors where they passed under some of the older lines. At the intersection of Broadway, Sixth Avenue and Thirty-third Street, Manhattan, we find a total of four sets of tunnels in three layers below an underground mezzanine; above these are busy surface streets and above them, in turn, we find still another artery in the form of an elevated railroad—five levels of transportation, one above the other!

Subway construction is seldom found to be the cause of disappearance of old landmarks. Yet cases do happen. At one point on the Queens route of the Eighth Avenue Subway it became necessary to demolish an old house that had stood for many years on property at the corner of Broadway and Elmhurst Avenue. Wrecking crews are not inclined to soliloquy nor to the loss of any tears over old landmarks. To them this was just "another old house" which had to make way for the subway construction. But to some others who had occasion to become familiar with its history, the destruction must have carried childhood visions of a "jolly old fellow" with his prancing reindeer. For it was the birthplace of Clement C. Moore who wrote *The Night before Christmas*.

\* \* \* \*

*Philadelphia's First Subway.*

Philadelphia's Market Street Subway at first promised to be an elevated line. At least that was the condition of the original franchise which was granted in 1901 and acquired by the "Union Traction Company" in 1902. Fortunately for the appearance of downtown Philadelphia, this predecessor of the present Philadelphia Rapid Transit Company obtained permission to change the plan to permit construction of the line as a subway through the city's business district. The rest of the route from the Schuylkill to Sixty-ninth Street remained elevated in accordance with the original proposal. The subway portion begins just east of the bridge carrying the route over the Schuylkill and it runs as a four-track line to City Hall, then continues as a double-track line east to Front Street, whence it again becomes an elevated line connecting with ferries. The original route was detoured around the City Hall, the eastbound tracks passing south of it and the westbound tracks north of it. Construction began in April of 1903, and the subway was opened for service on August 3, 1908, the line as far as Fifteenth Street having been in operation a few months earlier. The subway portion is two and one-quarter miles long and one of its distinctive features is the number of direct entrances from buildings, with cheery department store windows lining station sidewalls under East Market Street. Excavation of the East Market Street section brought to light some of the abandoned old wooden water pipes that had been laid in 1799 and consisted of hemlock logs with a six-inch hole bored through them. The wood was surprisingly sound despite its years of burial.

*Broad Street Subway.*

After completion of the Market Street subway, city officials began giving serious consideration to a municipal north-and-south line under Broad Street, to be designed by the city engineers and constructed under the direction of its Department of Transit. The first step toward attainment of this end was taken when a contract was awarded in 1915 for the "City Hall section" of what would eventually become a Broad Street subway. This covered only a very short section, about 750 feet to be more exact, passing under the massive City Hall and beneath the original subway. The work thus became so involved that it took something like four years to complete and proved to be about the most expensive piece of subway construction that has ever been undertaken, apart from underwater tunneling. The route lay directly under some of the tremendously heavy rubble foundations of the City Hall, and parts of these were found to be in very poor condition—consisting of massive stones laid together without mortar. Some portions had to be completely replaced with new foundations while, in the meantime, the load of the enormously heavy solid masonry building—built before the days of steel-frame structures —had to be transferred from the old support to a temporary one and then back again to the new permanent one. Even at that, the route had to be detoured slightly westward to avoid passing directly under City Hall tower, a heavy structure of masonry 548 feet high—

thus accounting for the peculiar "kink" in the route at this point. By the time this work was finished in 1919, residents were calling it the "million dollar hole in the ground." Perhaps the great cost of this short section had something to do with the fact that, for a few years, no further progress was made on the Broad Street project, and that it was August of 1924 before the next work had been started. From that time on, however, rapid progress was made. One contract followed another until the whole length from City Hall to Olney Avenue, about six miles, was under construction almost simultaneously. By September 1, 1928, the work had been practically completed and two of the four tracks were placed in operation over this distance, the line being operated by the Philadelphia Rapid Transit Company under a lease. In the meantime, an extension southward had been put under construction and in April of 1930 trains were operated through to South Street, making a total of six and a half miles of line, built by the city at a cost of about $109,000,000 plus an additional $11,000,000 for a spur from Broad Street via Ridge Avenue to the Eighth and Market Streets department-store district. A connection has been made from this spur to the Delaware River Bridge, permitting operation of a shuttle service between Philadelphia and Camden. Through trains now operate over this bridge by means of the new subway connecting at Race and Eighth Streets, thus giving Camden a direct subway connection with Philadelphia.

*Philadelphia's Underground City.*

With what promised to be its most important subway station placed right under City Hall, it became evident that operation of the new line would result in enormously increased interference with street traffic due to pedestrians crossing to and from this "island" station. Hence, a most comprehensive system of underground passageways was constructed in connection with building of the South Broad Street subway. But the system went further than merely providing passageways to the City Hall Station—plans were extended to include connections with many buildings in the downtown area and they gave to Philadelphia what is probably the most comprehensive system of underground pedestrian passageways in existence and certainly the most complete in this country. By the fall of 1936, most of the system was in operation, and as part of this plan the original Market Street subway tracks which looped around City Hall were removed, and trains are now operated through new tunnels running as straight as a die under the building. The changes were made without interrupting traffic and practically unnoticed by the passengers. Early one morning in May of 1936, the construction crews quickly ripped up a few lengths of the old curved track, slid two straight sections of ninety-pound rails into place, deftly bolted the joints and drove spikes home into the ties. Less than a minute later, a westbound Market Street train leaving Thirteenth Street Station rolled straight through on the

143

new line instead of swinging around the old loop that had been in use since the line was opened in 1908.

This change made the old subway train tunnels available for other uses and allowed the City Department of Transit to proceed with its plan to complete its pedestrian concourse system. The completed system now provides undercover, underground connection between three stations of the Market Street subway, three stations of the Broad Street subway, the new Pennsylvania Railroad underground suburban terminal, many large department stores, banks and hotels as well as innumerable office buildings. It is possible to walk underground from as far south as Spruce Street to as far north as Race Street, a distance of more than six city blocks. In the east-and-west direction, one can now walk underground for seven city blocks. One part of the system—the South Broad Concourse—is 100 feet wide, and, literally speaking, almost the whole central area of downtown Philadelphia can be reached without going out of doors. There is nothing of this kind quite so extensive anywhere else in America; even New York's underground connections at its two great railroad stations cannot begin to compare with this subterranean city that has just been built by the City of Philadelphia.

Fig. 24.—A junction in Chicago's freight subway, showing an electric locomotive and a freight car. (*Courtesy of Chicago Tunnel Company.*)

Fig. 25.—The tunnel builders' first dining car was used when building the Southern California Edison Company's Ward Tunnel.

(*Facing page* 144)

FIG. 26.—Placing concrete on a cut-and-cover portion of the Colorado River Aqueduct. Before the advent of modern excavating machinery this section would, most likely, have been constructed by tunneling under the surface.

FIG. 27.—Looking out through the portal of a tunnel on the Colorado River Aqueduct. (*Photographs courtesy of Metropolitan Water District.*)

*Chapter* XIV

# Some Biggest Things in Tunneling

*One of the Biggest Tunnel Projects.*

FROM the viewpoint of cost, the Pennsylvania Railroad's New York tunnels and terminal deserve to rank among the "biggest" tunneling projects. As early as 1885, this railroad had considered extension of its lines into New York by means of a bridge, and it became associated with the great structure proposed by Gustav Lindenthal in 1887. At that time, it should be noted, the problem of tunneling under the Hudson looked much farther from solution than the problem of bridging a 2,850- to 3,200-foot river without affecting its use as an important waterway. For many reasons the bridge plans made little progress and, by 1900, it was evident from the work of Pearson that a tunnel under the Hudson had become an engineering possibility. Hence, the Pennsylvania turned its interest from bridge schemes to ideas of a tunnel and its engineering investigations resulted in a decision to proceed along this course instead. Accordingly, on December 11, 1901, its "Pennsylvania New York Extension Railroad

145

Company" was incorporated in the State of New York for the purpose of carrying out a most comprehensive scheme of tunneling under both the Hudson and East Rivers, as well as constructing a monumental terminal on Manhattan into which both the Pennsylvania and the Long Island trains would run. The New York tunnel extension and terminal and the new yards at Harrison, New Jersey, and Sunnyside, Long Island, were estimated by the road's engineers at the grand total cost of about $100,000,000. Even this did not include the necessary electrification of certain sections of both roads, some improvements of the Long Island road in Brooklyn and construction of the New York Connecting Railway with its Hell Gate Bridge.

The New York Tunnel and Terminal portion of this great scheme was to provide for two single-tube tunnels under the Hudson, a vast passenger station in Manhattan, four single-tube tunnels under the East River and the necessary tunnels under Thirty-second and Thirty-third Streets to connect these with the new terminal facing on Seventh Avenue. Contracts for building the river tunnels were awarded in March of 1904, the Hudson River sections to O'Rourke Engineering and Contracting Company of New York and the East River sections to S. Pearson and Son of London. All the river tubes were to be built with tunneling shields and to consist of twenty-three-foot cast-iron shells lined on the inside with two feet of concrete.

146

*The Movement of Tunnels in Silt.*

At this time there was considerable doubt on the part of engineers as to the ability of the soft Hudson River silt to support a tube through which heavy trains were to run. So, with very creditable caution on the part of the railroad, the original design for these tubes called for a series of screw piles to help in carrying this load. After the iron shell of the tunnel was in place, these pipes were to be forced down through the silt to bedrock, holes being provided in the bottom plates for this purpose. At a later date, however, it was found that such precaution would be unnecessary. Both during and after construction surveys had been made to detect any change in the position of the completed tubes, which virtually float in mud. These investigations eventually extended over a period of several years and the information obtained proved to be as surprising as it was illuminating. Their results showed that tubes in this soft Hudson River silt actually do move; but they also showed that the change, being only a small fraction of an inch, was far too slight to be of any practical consequence. Indeed, the movement is very much less than is produced in a bridge structure when it expands and contracts with changes in temperature. Rather surprisingly, three different cycles of regular movement were found to exist. First, there was a slight change which took place twice a day, the tubes rising and falling (about an eighth of an inch) with the tides. Then another cycle (involving a movement of

147

slightly over a quarter of an inch) took place once a year, each tube rising in summer and sinking in winter. Still a third change took place in the form of a gradual settlement which, after the first several years, had diminished until it became negligible.

## A Monumental Work Is Finished.

The net result of the first measurements was that only one screw pile was installed, and that was only for experimental purposes. A decision to eliminate the screw piles was announced in July of 1908 by Vice-President Samuel Rea, himself an engineer. Doubtless his decision was influenced not alone by the studies but also by the fact that the Hudson and Manhattan Railroad tubes were already operating successfully under similar conditions. The entire project made such rapid progress that it stood out in sharp contrast with the interminable delays that arose in building the first Hudson tunnel. O'Rourke broke all speed records then existing for shield tunneling by starting the Pennsylvania tubes under the Hudson in February of 1905, bringing the north tube shields together under the River in September of 1906 and bringing the south pair together in October. The East River tubes followed, the first of these being holed through in February of 1908, and the second, third and fourth in March of the same year. The first public use of the great terminal— now one of the landmarks of New York City—was made in 1910. Curiously enough, the inaugural trip was not made by one of the Pennsylvania's own trains. Instead, it was made by one of its subsidiary. For, on September 8, 1910, a train of the Long Island Rail Road passed through one of the new tubes under the East River, rumbled through a tunnel under Manhattan and came to a stop at one of the new platforms. Thus, for the first time in its history, the Long Island Road delivered its passengers directly in the heart of New York instead of at its Long Island City ferry terminal. A short time after, the first Pennsylvania train sped through one of the tubes under the Hudson and came to a stop in the terminal. A few years later, with completion of the massive Hell Gate Bridge of the New York Connecting Railway, through trains from the north began using these East River tubes, the new terminal and the Hudson tubes, thus giving to Boston its first through passenger service to and from the south. And, with the inauguration of this last link, the Pennsylvania Railroad was able to announce the completion of its "New York Improvement"—a work that will go down in history as one of the greatest railroad tunnel undertakings in the world.

*Rove Canal Tunnel—the Largest in Volume.*

The Rove Tunnel on the Marseilles-Rhone Canal— cut through a mountain of limestone for a fraction over four and one-half miles to provide a connection between the River Rhone and the Port of Marseilles— has the greatest excavated volume of any one tunnel

**149**

ever constructed. This tunnel was built between 1911 and 1926 by the French Government and the Chamber of Commerce of Marseilles, with the latter supplying most of the funds. It is nearly semicircular in section, having a rectangular base seventy-two feet wide at the tow-path level, sixty feet at the water line, and an arched roof extending forty feet above the surface of its ten-foot-deep canal, the tunnel thus being fifty feet high in all. Construction began at the south end in 1911 and at the north end in 1914 but work was somewhat interrupted by the outbreak of the World War. Indeed, operations were completely suspended for a time and there were indications that it might never be resumed because of the tremendous cost of drilling such a large tunnel. After some delay, prisoners of war were put to work and construction was resumed, the first of the two advance headings being holed through in February of 1916. After some further delays, the tunnel was completed and put into use officially in 1927, having taken about fifteen years to construct and having cost 135,000,000 francs. Depreciation of the French currency having been in progress during the construction, it is impossible to convert this sum into American money with any degree of accuracy. It ranges somewhere between $5,500,000 and $37,000,000.

Although considerably shorter than several earlier tunnels, the immense area of the Rove made it necessary to excavate a much greater volume of material than was removed in building *any* of these, including even the Simplon. From the time of its opening in 1927 until the Goat Island Tunnel at San Francisco was opened in 1936, this Rove project held the record of having the largest bore of any one tunnel ever constructed. It still is the largest canal tunnel and, as we have said, has the greatest excavated volume of any tunnel in the world.

## The Goat Island Tunnel.

When the Rove Tunnel lost its place as the largest-bore tunnel, the record went to one forming just an incident in the construction of a tremendous bridge. This bridge is the one crossing San Francisco Bay in connection with which an enormous tunnel was bored through Goat Island to provide a link between its East Bay and West Bay sections. Rising some 345 feet above sea level, this island blocked the way of a connection between these two sections, although providing the best route in all other respects. The most practical solution was that of cutting a tunnel through the island and, since the bridge was to be a double-decked one, this necessitated a double-decked tunnel of unprecedented height. The net result was construction of a tunnel having a cross section that exceeded even that of the Rove. The Goat Island bore measured fifty-eight feet wide and seventy-six feet high "in the rough," or fifty-two by sixty-six feet inside its concrete lining. Being only 540 feet long, it required much less excavation than the Rove and many other tunnels,

151

but its *area* exceeded that of any. In fact, its size was such that one of the "pilot" or advance tunnels (which were cut first) measured fourteen by fourteen feet— enough to allow the passage of a train. Yet this, as well as two smaller tunnels, was drilled merely to facilitate excavation of rock in driving through the full-sized tunnel. The full-size bore is big enough to enclose a six-story apartment building.

*Some Other "Biggest" Tunnels.*

There are many tunnels and subways which can lay claim to being the "biggest" in one form or another and some of these have been described elsewhere in this volume. So far as cost is concerned, the $220,000,000 Colorado River Aqueduct and the $246,000,000 Catskill Water Scheme can undoubtedly take their places at the top of the list. Indeed, the Catskill figure does not include the extension to the Delaware watershed which is now under construction. From the viewpoint of length, San Francisco's twenty-five-mile Coast Range Tunnel is now the longest continuous tunnel in existence, although it will be exceeded when New York's forty-five-mile Delaware Aqueduct Tunnel is finished. When it comes to subway mileage, New York heads the list with its several networks showing a combined total of 136 miles of underground routes. Liverpool's "Queensway" is both the largest shield tunnel and the largest underwater tunnel ever built. The highest tunnel is probably one on the TransAndean Railway, which passes through a mountain at a point almost 12,000 feet above sea level. So far as variety of trouble is concerned, this rather doubtful honor certainly belongs to the Tanna Tunnel in Japan although—if we include the first efforts—London's Thames Tunnel took the longest period to build. From the point of view of construction speed, the subways in Moscow and Buenos Aires take the lead, six miles of the former having been completed in about one year and four and a half miles of the latter in a year and three-quarters.

## A Tremendous Tunnel That Was Never Built.

While on this subject of large tunnels, it might be appropriate to mention something about the largest tunnel that was ever seriously proposed, even though it never got beyond the "blueprint" stage. This came up in 1879 in connection with one of the many plans to cut a canal from the Atlantic to the Pacific through the central American isthmus, several of the proposals having included large tunnels. One of these, the San Blas route, would have required a gigantic tunnel, much larger than any that has ever been built since. It was to run at least seven miles through a mountain and would have depth and clearance sufficient for the largest ocean vessels of that date. This called for a tunnel through solid rock, 168 feet high from the bottom of the twenty-eight-foot-deep canal to the top of the arch and a hundred feet wide at the water line. The estimated cost of the canal was given, in 1879, as about

$67,000,000. Goat Island Tunnel at San Francisco, had a cross section of about 4,000 square feet before it was lined; the greatest tunnel excavation up to date was that of the Rove Canal Tunnel in France, where 2,250,000 cubic yards of material had to be removed. In comparison with these, the San Blas tunnel would have had a cross section of about 14,000 square feet and its excavation would have entailed the removal of at least 19,200,000 cubic yards of rock! Certainly, it would be a gigantic undertaking for the present, let alone for more than half a century ago. Selection of the Panama route for the interocean canal, wrote "finis" on this ambitious San Blas idea with its gigantic tunnel.

## Chapter XV

# Tunneling for Power and Irrigation

*The Gunnison Tunnel.*

DURING the development of Federal irrigation projects in different parts of the United States, it became necessary to bore a number of long water tunnels. In fact, up to December of 1930, the Bureau of Reclamation of the Department of the Interior had constructed no less than 124 tunnels aggregating about thirty-three and one-half miles in length. Most of these were tunneling projects of some magnitude, one of the first being the Gunnison Tunnel, built between 1905 and 1910 as part of the Uncompahgre Valley irrigation plan. By diversion of the waters of the Gunnison River through this six-mile tunnel and a twelve-mile canal, a desert waste in Colorado is being converted into fertile country. The Gunnison is a "man-size" tunnel, eleven feet wide and over ten feet high in the concrete-lined portion. At other parts, where the solidity of the rock eliminated the necessity of a concrete lining, the tunnel is even larger, being about twelve and one-half feet wide and thirteen feet high. Thus, so far as size and length are concerned, it compares with many railroad

155

tunnels. It is rather interesting to find that one part
of this tunnel passes through a thick bed of sea shells,
showing that the area, at some prehistoric time, must
have been under the sea. Work of construction began
in February of 1905, but, owing to construction difficulties and financial troubles, the contractor abandoned
the job a short time later and it was carried through
to completion by day labor under the direction of
government engineers. Considerable trouble was encountered with many a cave-in resulting from soft
ground and water. In one of these twenty-one men were
entombed, but all were rescued about twenty-five hours
later. At a certain point, one of the headings passed
through a rock fault where water came in at the rate of
5,000,000 gallons a day. So far as irrigation needs were
concerned, this volume of water might have been very
welcome, and good use could have been made of it.
To the tunnel builders, it was anything but good news;
in fact, it made considerable trouble for them before
the construction had passed beyond this point. However, these problems were finally mastered, and on
September 23, 1909, the completed tunnel was officially
opened by President Taft.

*Boulder Dam Diversion Tunnels.*

Many tunnels followed this one, the greatest of them
from many viewpoints being the large diversion tunnels
built in connection with the construction of Boulder
Dam. These consist of four enormous holes cut through

156

solid rock for a distance of about three-fourths of a mile in order to divert the entire waters of the Colorado River during the period necessary for construction of the big dam at Black Canyon on the Arizona-Nevada state line. After completion of the project the tunnels will continue in use, conveying water to the hydro-electric plant below the dam. These four tunnels are each fifty-six feet in diameter in the rough, or fifty-feet net inside their concrete lining. In area they are exceeded only by the Rove Canal Tunnel in France and the Goat Island Tunnel of the San Francisco Bay Bridge. Their great sectional area necessitated the construction of an enormous drilling "rig" to facilitate the job of boring such a large hole through hard rock. This drilling "jumbo," as the workers and engineers called it, consisted of a steel frame carrying five horizontal bars upon which were mounted as many as thirty rock drills for simultaneous use. A drilling crew amounting to forty-five men could work at one time on this great movable platform.

Underground work on these tunnels did not begin until May of 1931, although the contractors had been at work some time earlier, constructing roads leading to the tunnel portals and installing their compressor plants for supplying air to the pneumatic drills. In themselves, the Boulder Dam tunnels involved no unusual engineering problems beyond those resulting from their unusual size. Neither did their builders have to master some of the construction difficulties that were met in drilling some of the long railroad tunnels that we have described. By 1932, the diversion tunnels had been holed through and the work of putting in a concrete lining was under way. This developed into somewhat of a race against time in order to permit use of the tunnels before the spring floods. Even a short delay in completing the tunnels would have necessitated a much longer wait for return of favorable conditions to permit construction of the dam itself. To resist the great pressure of water within the tunnels after going into service, the concrete lining had to be made three feet thick. This probably established a record for normal thickness in concrete tunnel linings. Between the unusual thickness and the combined length of more than three miles for all four tunnels, the lining required about 300,000 cubic yards of concrete.

*A Huge Tunneling Job.*

To give some conception of the volume of concrete involved, picture a gigantic monolith constructed with the same material upon a base that measures 100 by 100 feet. To equal the amount used in lining the Boulder Dam tunnels, this would have to extend straight up, one solid mass without even a setback, to a height of 810 feet—18 feet more than the height of New York's famous sixty-story Woolworth Building! Quantities of other materials became equally staggering to the imagination. Each blast for a main heading took 1,800 pounds of dynamite, almost a ton, to load the forty-eight holes that were drilled as much as twenty feet into the rock face. This was fired in fifteen "delays" or series and in a sequence planned to break out the greatest amount of rock with the least explosives. With each blast the headings were extended 16 feet farther, and about 2,160 *tons of rock were broken out.* The last section of these four tunnels was holed through on May 23, 1932—a year and nine days from the date of starting. During this period, something like 1,500,000 cubic yards of rock had been blasted out and removed from the tunnel. Intense heat made work anything but pleasant for the construction forces during the summer, the canyon attaining a temperature of 128 degrees in the shade!

## *Tunneling for Water Power.*

While the government was tunneling for irrigation water, many large electric power companies were drilling tunnels to supply their turbines with great streams of water at high velocity. Sometimes the water is brought down from such a great height that the pressure forces it out of the turbine nozzles at terrific speed, and the jet can be struck with a hammer only to have the tool rebound as if it had been driven against solid steel instead of rapidly moving water. Electricity, of course, is not to be found by mining for it as one would mine for coal, yet the result is about the same, for it was often only the boring of a long tunnel through rock that made it possible to tap the potential power

159

which, otherwise, would have remained unavailable. One of the more recent power tunnels at Niagara Falls is thirty-two feet inside, or wider than the average double-track railroad tunnel.

Some power companies took up tunneling in a big way. As part of the Southern California Edison Company's Big Creek Project, it became necessary to bore, through Kaiser Ridge, a tunnel fifteen feet in diameter and about thirteen and one-half miles long. This was originally called the "Florence Lake Tunnel," because it taps Florence Lake high up in the Sierras and brings this water to Huntington Lake Reservoir, from which it is carried through pipes and tunnels to several electric power plants. After its completion, the name was changed to "Ward Tunnel" in honor of the late George C. Ward, former president of the Company and moving genius behind the whole gigantic project. And "gigantic" is the only word that fits this case for the whole system really includes a chain of six dams, eight tunnels and five power plants, representing in all, an initial investment of about $150,000,000! But it is the thirteen and one-half-mile Ward Tunnel that interests us chiefly here, because of the scale of tunneling for a water-power project. Work on the Big Creek Development began in 1911, and it took until 1929 to bring to its present stage of completion. The Ward Tunnel was begun in the summer of 1920 and, by working right through days and nights, it was completed in 1925. Work was carried on from each end and also in each

Fig. 28.—This is what subway builders find when they start to excavate city streets; all these pipes must be moved to new locations before they can proceed.

Fig. 29.—Sinking a caisson to form one of the Holland Tunnel shafts. This great structure of steel and concrete was worked down through the river bed until it reached solid rock, the "muck" being excavated by diggers working in the compressed-air chamber formed by the lowest portion. After the caisson reached its final seat upon solid rock, the bottom was sealed with concrete and the air pressure removed. This structure remains in place and forms one of the ventilation shafts, the tunnel tubes passing through it by means of the round openings which are shown here as temporarily closed and braced. (*Photographs courtesy of The Port of New York Authority.*)

Fig. 30.—A partly finished portion of the Holland Tunnel showing the fresh-air duct below the floor, the roadway tube in the center and the vitiated-air duct above it.

Fig. 31.—Interior of the completed Holland Tunnel. (*Photographs courtesy of The Port of New York Authority.*)

direction from two intermediate "adits," or horizontal passages, cut into the mountains from two valleys. This tunnel had to be driven through hard granite nearly all the way, and the blasting took about 5,200,-000 pounds of explosives. Even more vividly illustrating the scale of this operation is another figure appearing in one of the tables in the engineers' report upon its construction. This is just the bare statement that "1,150,000 pounds of drill steel were used" in the construction work. Five hundred and seventy-five tons of hard steel drills worn to dust by pounding against the granite interior of Kaiser Ridge!

*Dog Teams to Maintain Communication.*

The force of workers ranged from a minimum of 500 men in 1920 to a maximum of 2,000 in 1924. To feed this army required a thoroughly organized commissary department, and, because of the isolated locations at elevations around 7,000 feet up in the air, snow became a major problem. Two thousand men were snowed in for most of each winter, necessitating most unusual arrangements to maintain contact with civilization. For the winter months of each year, the construction forces borrowed an idea from Alaskan prospectors. Dog teams and sleds were used to carry the mails and some light essentials to and from the camps in winter. It seems hard to realize that these men working their way through the granite mountain and living in bunkhouses in the midst of heavy snowdrifts—with every

161

aspect of Northern Alaska in midwinter—were less than 270 miles from the always-balmy middays of Los Angeles! To supply power for the construction required building a 30,000-volt electric line up into the mountains and cutting through miles of truck roads. Even a railroad was built from El Prado, east of Fresno, to Cascada, where the headquarters camp was located.

### The Tunnel-Builders' "Dining Car."

The Ward Tunnel brought many innovations, including the first recorded use of a "dining-car" construction train in a tunnel. This interesting feature resulted from the great and ever-growing distance between the portals and the headings as the work went on and the crews bored their way farther into the granite mountain. At the time that this dining car story broke upon an interested world, the workers were about two miles into the mountain. By this time, traveling back and forth for lunch was almost out of the question. Supervisors of the work concluded that cold lunches combined with the strenuous labor of rock drillers and muckers were not going to be conducive to maintenance of good health—particularly when their men had to go from the hot damp air of the underground tunnel out into the cold blasts of the upper Sierras in midwinter. So the outcome was the first tunnel-builders' dining cars. A train was made up of five cars, three having simple board tables with a line of stools on each

162

side while the other two bore "fireless cookers" to keep the food hot during the few-mile trip from the camp kitchen outside in the snows. The hot meal was provided by the company in the interests of that increased efficiency which always follows better working conditions. Two waiters traveled with the train to set the tables, serve the workers and clean up after each meal.

As construction went on it became necessary to carry the compressed-air lines 19,000 feet from the power plant into the mountain before the opposite headings met. Ventilation also became a problem, so pipes 2 feet in diameter were carried as much as 10,000 feet into the tunnel to ensure adequate fresh air for the workers. The finished tunnel is capable of carrying no less than 2,500 cubic feet of water per second—about fifty-five per cent more than the capacity of the great Colorado River Aqueduct described elsewhere in this book. So hard was the rock that only eleven per cent of the tunnel had to be lined with concrete, the rest was in granite hard enough to withstand the wear of countless years of water rushing through. With the system of dams, tunnels and power plants complete, the melting snows and rainfalls of the Sierras will turn their energies into power and light for the homes, offices and factories of Southern California. And instead of madly rushing torrents raging on their way to the sea each spring, the tamed waters will spread their flow evenly throughout the year, eliminating flood hazard

163

in spring and ensuring water through summer to the eternal benefit of the many thousands of cultivated acres in the lowlands. But the strangest part of this story is that so many of these water-power projects turn into schemes whereby the engineers have to tunnel their way into a mountain to tap the source—virtually mining for power!

## Chapter XVI

# The First "Trench" Tunnels

*Some Original Ideas.*

THE idea of laying a tunnel upon the bottom of a waterway is far from being new. Indeed, suggestions along
these lines appeared before 1854, when a pamphlet
had been circulated under the title of "Miller's Submarine Avenue." This described a plan for constructing
tunnels by laying a cast-iron shell upon the bed of a
river just as a pipe might be laid; the whole structure
was to be anchored in place to keep it from floating
to the surface. History has little else to say about
Miller, and his scheme might have remained in oblivion
also had not the eminent engineer Drinker taken
occasion to mention it as "a type of the many wild
designs put forth." Little did Drinker imagine that the
basic principles of Miller's "wild" scheme were, some
forty years later, to be put into practical use in constructing a nine-foot trunk sewer under Boston Harbor
in 1893–1894 and, in 1906–1910 to the Michigan
Central's new tunnel under the Detroit River to provide
a direct route into the City of Detroit. There must
have been something about this preconstructed-and-

sunk tunnel idea that gave it an especial appeal to
inventors. For it was forgotten, resurrected and again
forgotten with amazing frequency. Indeed, one is
surprised that so many of the later re-inventors had
never heard about the plans of their predecessors. The
*Scientific American* of April 4, 1857, described a plan
of one Joseph de Sendzimir of South Oyster Bay,
Long Island, New York, for building underriver tunnels
by laying an iron tube on the bed of a river and weight-
ing it down, a "submarine thoroughfare" he called it.
He proposed to float into place an assembled tube
designed with a flat bottom and a domed top; this
would be sunk until it rested upon the river bed,
whereupon enough weight would be applied to hold
it there.

Two months later the same magazine, gave space to a
description of the plan of H. P. Holcomb, a civil
engineer of Winchester, Georgia, for laying a tunnel
of iron pipe upon the bed of a river. The story, however,
failed to include anything about Holcomb's proposed
construction methods. About ten years passed and in
1867 *The Engineer* of London published a letter from
a correspondent, J. J. Morris, claiming to have invented a plan of preconstructing tunnels, floating
them into place in sections, sinking the sections and
then pumping the water out after the work was otherwise completed. This, he said, was described previously
in a publication of his which had appeared about eleven
years earlier.

*Floating Tunnel Proposed.*

Still another variety of the "built-and-sunk" tunnel made its appearance in a proposal of 1870. J. L. Haddan, Director of Public Works at Aleppo, a city in North Syria, recommended to the Turkish Government a unique plan for constructing a tunnel under the Bosphorus. The water there is very deep, running as much as 120 feet, and is underlaid with another twenty or thirty feet of very soft mud. These and other considerations having combined to make the then usual method of construction impossible, Haddan proposed to sink a floating tunnel. Its top was to be about thirty-five feet beneath the surface and at this height he would securely anchor it to prevent movement. The weight of the tunnel, added to that of the trains using it, was to be less than the weight of the displaced water. Thus it would retain its buoyancy when carrying a fully loaded train; only the anchorage was to prevent it from floating to the surface. The tunnel was to be ten feet in diameter and constructed of heavy wrought iron plates to form a pipe 1,200 feet long. A working model of the Haddan scheme was built for the Turkish Government but the plan was not taken up. No tunnel was ever built at this crossing nor has the Haddan floating-tunnel scheme ever been used elsewhere. A couple of years later, almost exactly the same scheme was proposed by some others as a means of providing a crossing under San Francisco Bay. By 1876, the constant recurrence of different "build-and-sink" schemes

167

must have had its effect upon the inherent conservatism of some leading engineers. For in this year, the *Engineering News* carried the announcement of a patent granted in August of that year to the eminent engineer, John C. Trautwine. Trautwine's patent covered a plan for constructing a tunnel upon a wooden platform above water, trenching the bottom of the river, then sinking the preconstructed tunnel into this trench (in short sections if necessary) and covering the structure over. The 1876 editor's reaction to this patent was illuminating in the extreme. Calmly ignoring the ridicule cast upon built-and-sunk tunnel schemes by earlier engineers, he proceeded to express his objection to Trautwine's patenting of the method by calling it a design that any "good engineer would be sure to adopt in a proper location"! All of this goes to show how even expert opinion can change with the times.

### The First "Built-and-sunk" Tunnel.

Starting from this period, the attitude of engineers toward preconstructed tunnels began to change. In 1885, Hayden H. Hall built 1,230 feet of double water mains across Sydney Harbour by using one of the many variations of the "build-and-sink" process. Hall's scheme was novel in the extreme. He used a traveling caisson or box that moved along the bed of the bay. Work began at one side and the first sections of his tube were assembled upon shore. When the water edge was reached, he brought his moving box into use.

Placing it over the end of the already completed part of the tube on shore, additional sections of the tube then assembled inside the box and attached to the previous ones. The entire box was then moved forward by means of jacks pressing against the end of the tube, the whole box sliding ahead as the finished tube passed out through a watertight connection at the rear. The next section was then connected and the forward movement repeated. The pipe sections were of heavy cast iron with sufficient weight to eliminate all tendency to float up to the surface when empty. While this was the first preconstructed tunnel, it remained for 1893 to see the start of the first tunnel constructed somewhat in accordance with present "build-and-sink" practice and large enough for a man to walk through. This happened when a nine-foot water main was built across Boston Harbor by H. A. Carson. Sections fifty-two feet long were constructed on shore, floated to over the exact site and sunk into a trench which had been dredged to receive them. These sections were of brick and concrete with a wood skin. The job, completed in 1894, is believed to be the first practical construction of its kind and one that established the method for many following. Several years later the Harlem River tubes of New York's first subway were built from a plan having some resemblance to these methods. Only, in this case, the roof was all that the builders sunk into place; the rest of the work was constructed under the protection of this roof.

*Detroit River Tunnel.*

About 1905–1906 the Michigan Central Railroad was giving serious consideration to plans for tunneling the Detroit River in order to eliminate the necessity of transferring all its growing passenger traffic by ferry over the river from Windsor. Being rather open-minded regarding the choice of construction methods, the road's board of consulting engineers, headed by Col. Wm. J. Wilgus, asked prospective contractors to bid upon any one of several alternative methods. By the time that all bids had been studied, it was very evident that a "build-and-sink" proposal would result in the lowest cost to the road. Hence cost determined its choice and the Michigan Central Railroad proceeded to make history by constructing the first large tunnel built by this method. The work began in the fall of 1906 amid an air of scepticism in engineering circles. Not much over a year had passed before it was evident that the Butler Brothers Construction Company, builder of this tunnel, was proceeding to confound the critics. For a method so novel, the work went along with celerity and was carried successfully through to completion in about four years. This double-tube tunnel was built by constructing the tubes in ten sections, each 262 feet long with a "closing" section sixty-four feet long. Side by side in pairs, these sections were then built into wooden caissons or boxes which were open top and bottom. In the meantime, a trench thirty to fifty feet deep was dredged in the bed of the

170

river to a width of forty-eight feet. Upon completion of each section of this trench, one of the caissons bearing its pair of tubes was floated into position and then sunk until it rested upon temporary foundations previously built at each joint near the trench bottom. Concrete was then applied around the tubes by simply filling up the box while it rested upon the bottom under water. After this, the river bed material was replaced to provide a cover over the finished work.

As each section was sunk and set in position it was joined to the previous one. When all had been sunk, connected together and concreted, the water was pumped out from inside and the interior also was lined with concrete. The first of these boxes was sunk into position on October 1, 1907, and work proceeded without serious interruption until the tunnel was opened in 1910. On September 18th of that year, the first regular freight train passed through the tunnel; starting October 16, both freight and passenger trains were routed through it to the new Michigan Central Terminal in Detroit, the change taking place without any special recognition. So thus, without ceremony or formality, there went into service the first railroad tunnel constructed completely by this method which, only half a century before, had been ridiculed as a visionary and "wild idea" by some of the most capable engineers of that earlier day.

## Chapter XVII

# Two Tunnels in Japan and Some in Italy

*Tanna Tunnel, the Champion Troublemaker.*

IN 1918 the Imperial Government Railways of Japan started work upon the Atami route, a thirty-mile cutoff designed to eliminate heavy grades on its Tokaido line—a project including a five-mile double-tracked tunnel which, before its completion, was to establish a new high mark in tunnel-builders' troubles. The new line was planned to reduce the distance between Tokyo and Kobe, one of Japan's important industrial centers, and thus was a route forming an important part of the railway system. The Tanna was started from each end with nothing to indicate either the unparalleled troubles which the engineers were going to face or the remarkably long time of sixteen years which would be required to complete the work. During this long period of construction, the builders encountered about every kind of trouble that could have been anticipated, as well as many which they had no cause to expect. Collapse of loose earth that buried workers alive; heavy inrushes of water at pressures ranging up to 275 pounds per square inch; clay that seemed as hard as rock when first excavated but which, when exposed to air, rapidly swelled and crushed heavy timbering; hard soil which absorbed water and then flowed suddenly like thin mud; water temperatures that reached ninety-seven degrees Fahrenheit—these were typical of the tunnel-builders' troubles. Efforts to combat them required the use of cement grouting, compressed air, tunneling shields, parallel drainage tunnels and about every modern aid of the tunnel builder. The loss of life was heavy, totalling at least seventy workers, with news reports constantly reciting one collapse after another as unexpected conditions developed. In April of 1921, 200 feet of rock roof suddenly fell, burying thirty-three men, of which only seventeen were later rescued, and these were saved only after eight days of strenuous work. In February of 1924, the earth suddenly gave way in another section, allowing soft mud to enter the heading and smothering or drowning sixteen men before anything could be done to save them. In February of 1929, heavy steel beams were reported as buckling under the irresistible force of the swelling clay. At another stage an entire tunneling shield was buried under a slide. Indeed, the combination of difficulties encountered was, and still remains, entirely without precedent in tunneling. It seemed as though every kind of trouble that has plagued tunnel builders through the ages had occasion to appear at one time or another in this single job.

173

*Every Conceivable Difficulty.*

Although the work had been started in April of 1918, the middle of 1929 saw it still only about three-fourths completed. Because of the enormous ground pressures encountered in some parts of the tunnel, it had become necessary to line these with concrete ranging from two feet to *six and a quarter feet thick* at the top of the arch—by a substantial margin the thickest tunnel lining that has ever been required since tunnels were first built. As the two opposite headings were nearing each other inside the mountain, the troubles assumed increased vigor; at this stage, the outstanding troubles were with high-pressure water, which, to add another problem, was coming in at a high temperature. It was appearing in such volume that the headings became unworkable, and drastic measures were necessary to drain this flood away. At first, the engineers started to cut a parallel side tunnel within the mountain, intending to tap the water supply and draw enough away to make the main heading workable. In a short time, water was coming into this side tunnel at a rate that closely rivalled that of the main heading. So another side tunnel was begun in the hope of draining more water through it. Still more water came in, and still another side tunnel was begun. Thus the fight went on, and, by the time they had succeeded in getting the water sufficiently under control to resume work in the main heading, the inside of the mountain was honeycombed with a network of short tunnels. As many as five parallel tunnels existed at some points! At times, the drainage tunnels were carrying away such torrents of water that the tunnel workers stood about as much chance of drowning as of being buried alive by another collapse! But the Japanese are a determined race. With the backing of their Government Railways, the engineers had started to tunnel this mountain, and, difficulties or not, they were determined that the work was to be finished. Eventually, this spirit of persistence won out—but not before the construction had cost seventy lives and vast sums of money. In 1934 the tunnel was completed, and about the end of that year it was opened for service, with the unenviable record of having made more trouble for its builders than any other tunnel in history.

While the Tanna was still under construction, another long tunnel in Japan was begun and finished. This was the six-mile Shimizu Tunnel started in 1922 and now longest in the country. Construction began at the south end in May of 1922 and on the north end in October of 1923. This job, however, did not prove to be a repetition of the Tanna, for the two headings met in December of 1929 and the tunnel was completed in August of 1931.

## "*Bologna-Firenze Direttissima.*"

The Bologna-Florence Direct Railroad is a fifty-one-mile line which was built to provide a more direct route between northern and central Italy. Running through very mountainous country, it has, within this short distance, no less than twenty-one tunnels as well as twenty-eight bridges or viaducts. The route, indeed, is almost one continuous series of tunnels, bridges and viaducts. Although originally planned as early as 1882, construction was not actually begun until 1913 and soon after that it became interrupted and much delayed by the World War. It was 1920 before work could be resumed, but, from that time on, it was pushed steadily ahead until the completion and official opening of the route in April of 1934. Of its twenty-one tunnels, the longest is the eleven-and-a-half-mile, double-tracked Apennine Tunnel which is second only to the Simplon among the world's long railroad tunnels. Because of its great length, a large "station" was built inside the mountain, two long sidings being provided for side-tracking of freight trains to permit the passage of fast passenger expresses. This underground station consists of two single-track tunnels, each about 1,970 feet long, paralleling the main tunnel and connected with it. Construction of the Apennine Tunnel alone cost about $40,000,000 and its builders encountered trouble with high-pressure water and with highly inflammable gases which became quite an explosion hazard at times. In addition to the Apennine and several short tunnels, the "Direttissima" also has one four-and-a-half-mile tunnel and another almost two miles long. The new route saves travelers between north and central Italy about an hour and a half because it eliminates a long and hard climb over the Appenine pass.

176

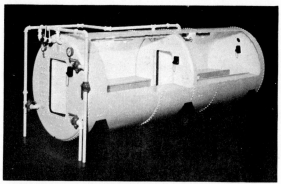

Fig. 32.—A hospital air lock is used in treatment of cases of "the bends" resulting from over exposure to air pressure. The sufferer is placed in the inner compartment of a special lock (as shown by this cut-away model) where he is resubjected to air pressure and the pressure is then decreased very gradually. The outer compartment serves as an air lock to permit a doctor or nurse to enter or leave the inner one without subjecting the patient to a change of pressure.

Fig. 33.—A gang of workers in an air lock undergoing decompression at the end of their shift in building the Lincoln Tunnel. These workers entered this lock from the tunnel end, closing the door after them. The air pressure in the lock is now being decreased very slowly because this has been found necessary to eliminate cases of "bends," a form of cramps resulting from too rapid release of nitrogen that became dissolved in the blood during exposure to the compressed air. (*Photographs courtesy of The Port of New York Authority.*)

Fig. 34.—Building a water tunnel for the Ford Motor Company's River Rouge power plant. These great concrete blocks interlocked with each other when placed in position and the completed shell was lined inside with a monolithic layer of concrete to make it watertight.

Fig. 35.—A close-up showing the "business end" of the hydraulically-operated erector as it lifts into place one of the 3,100-pound segments of the Lincoln Tunnel. (*Courtesy of The Port of New York Authority.*)

# Chapter XVIII

# Pacific Coast Aqueducts

*Miles of Aqueduct—Because the Sea Is Salt.*

JUST because we cannot drink salt water, there arises the curious situation of seacoast cities having to go hundreds of miles for water, although it lies at their doors. San Francisco is nearly surrounded by water; Los Angeles and its dozen neighboring cities are close to the sea. Yet San Francisco had to reach 170 miles inland to the Sierra Mountains while the others are going almost 400 miles to the Colorado River for adequate supplies of fresh water. Both projects are gigantic—the San Francisco development costing about $105,000,000 and the Southern California project around $220,000,000. In each case the first plans were conceived many years before actual construction began. Flow of water from the mountains to San Francisco involved considerable drop in elevation, so a water-power scheme was made part of this plan and several power plants have been constructed at the foot of mountains along the aqueduct. Los Angeles and its neighbors were not so fortunate. Quite the contrary indeed, for they will have to pump their water uphill at five points along the route.

*Hetch Hetchy Project.*

Under the direction of City Engineer M. M. O'Shaughnessy, San Francisco's Hetch Hetchy project—named after the valley forming its principal reservoir—was begun in 1914 with the start of construction of a standard-gauge railroad sixty-eight miles long. This was necessary for the transportation of men, materials and equipment for construction of water tunnels and the main dam at the Hetch Hetchy reservoir site. To carry water from this point to San Francisco, a whole series of tunnels had to be drilled through several intervening mountain ranges. Most important of these were the "Mountain Division" tunnels totalling about nineteen miles, the "Foothills" tunnels totalling about fifteen and three-quarters miles and the "Coast Range" tunnels including one three-and-a-half-mile tunnel and one twenty-five-mile continuous tunnel. The latter is the longest continuous tunnel in the world. All of these had to be driven through solid rock. Generally they measure about thirteen and a half feet by fourteen and a quarter feet in their unlined portions running through hard granite; inside the concrete-lined sections in other material they are about three feet less. Construction brought the usual variety of problems that always seem to attend work of this character. One of

178

the Foothills tunnels, started in March of 1926, involved serious trouble with water which came in under high pressure, reaching 350 and 400 pounds to the square inch. Extensive cement grouting had to be done before this leakage could be stopped and the work carried on. At one time, water came into this tunnel through a single drill hole at the rate of 500 gallons per minute and grouting pressures up to 625 pounds per square inch had to be used.

*Escaping Gases Make More Trouble.*

Another kind of trouble ensued when the highly explosive methane gas appeared in headings of the Coast Range tunnels, escaping from crevices in dangerous quantities. In the summer of 1930, a serious explosion resulted in the death of twelve men. After this, work was suspended until special safeguards could be taken to eliminate any possibility of a repetition of the disaster. Sulphuretted hydrogen, a gas with an odor reminiscent of thoroughly rotten eggs, appeared at another stage of work in this same tunnel. This gas caused trouble of a distinctly original kind; when inhaled by the workers, it became absorbed in their blood and produced a condition of temporary blindness. So precautions were taken to remove it as fast as it appeared. The last rock barrier of the Foothills was holed through in December of 1928 and that of the last Coast Range section in January of 1934. During this

179

period, the direction of construction was taken over by the San Francisco Public Utilities Commission, and, by October of 1934, water was flowing through these tunnels to the city.

While working in one of the tunnels during October of 1930, quicksand was encountered very suddenly, entering the tunnel without warning and forcing the men to flee for their lives. In just a few minutes, the water-laden sand completely filled about 2,500 feet of tunnel. That most peculiar and dreaded phenomenon, which is known to tunnel men as "swelling ground," also caused trouble for the workers in the Coast Range tunnels. Some material through which they had bored their way showed the most remarkable ability to close up soon after being excavated. In these places the ground swelled as soon as it was opened, forcing them to use rings of concrete instead of the customary timbers. Even then, some difficulty was found in holding the ground in place until the permanent concrete lining could be installed. In the last 600 feet of tunnel driven, it was actually necessary to keep this concrete away from the sides of the hole in order to allow it time to harden before the ground could swell enough to crush it like an eggshell. A clear space of at least a foot had to be left between the soil and this concrete; the ground swelled that much even in the short time required for a quicksetting cement to harden. An eighteen-foot hole cut through this soil squeezed down overnight to as little as twelve feet!

*The Colorado River Aqueduct.*

Some years ago, when the City of Los Angeles began to plan a water supply from the Colorado River, it was soon realized that many other cities in Southern California also required more water. Hence there came into existence "The Metropolitan Water District of Southern California," a distinct governmental division of the state. This district, including thirteen cities in Los Angeles and Orange Counties, is the builder and operator of the Colorado River Aqueduct. The project itself includes a total of 242 miles of main canal aqueducts, conduits and tunnels to bring the waters of the Colorado River from Parker Dam to the Cajalco reservoir. From here, another 150 miles of aqueduct is necessary to carry the water to the various cities, making a total trip of 392 miles in all. The Metropolitan Water District was created as a public corporation in 1928; plans which had been in the making since 1923 were then completed, and the work of construction began in December of 1932 under the direction of F. E. Weymouth as General Manager and Chief Engineer. The entire project became a gigantic venture, representing an investment of about $220,000,000, employing as many as 12,000 men at one time and forming one of the biggest construction jobs in history. To carry on the aqueduct construction, it was necessary to open up a 200-mile stretch of inaccessible mountain and desert country. Hundreds of miles of water mains, trunk roadways and high-tension electric power lines

had to be built. The main aqueduct involved a total of
108 miles of tunnels with another fifty-five miles of
cut-and-cover aqueduct construction. Conditions ranged
from the drilling of tunnels through hard blue granite
to surface excavation of dry gravel for the cut-and-
cover work in a sun-baked desert where extensive
sprinkling was necessary to keep the dust under
control.

## Pumping Out an Underground River.

Most of the main tunnels are sixteen feet clear inside,
only the two western ones being a few inches smaller.
The eighteen-mile East Coachella Tunnel is longest of
those involved in this construction and the thirteen-
mile San Jacinto is next. All tunnels are concrete lined
and some portions of the aqueduct are great concrete
tubes built in deep trenches and covered after completion so that they, also, end as tunnels. The usual water
troubles were encountered in some of the rock tunnels,
Potrero east heading of the San Jacinto tunnel at one
period taking in 14,500 gallons of water a minute, or
practically an underground river. Such enormous
volume would have meant complete defeat of the
builders only a few generations earlier. Here it was
removed as rapidly as it came in, an underground
pumping station being built in the tunnel and equipped
with powerful and efficient modern machinery which
had comparatively little difficulty in handling this
enormous flow of water. The cut-and-cover sections

of this aqueduct involved construction of a total of fifty-five miles of sixteen- by nineteen-foot "pipe"— large enough to clear a subway train or to provide a double-lane roadway under a lofty ceiling. Most of this was built across desert land where high temperatures often made working conditions unbearable. As a grudging concession to this desert heat, concreting operations were suspended in June, July, August and September. To protect the work, a careful study had to be made of the temperatures existing within this concrete while it was setting and whitewash coatings were applied to the surface of recently poured work in order to reflect the sunlight and thus prevent too much heating. All these precautions were necessary to prevent too rapid evaporation of the water in the concrete mixture while it was hardening and to prevent different temperatures from causing cracks.

## Chapter XIX

# The Holland Tunnel Sets a Pattern

*First "Motor Age" Tunnel.*

THE Holland Tunnel was an outgrowth of the motor age. It is distinctly a tunnel planned for motor vehicles; consequently, it set a precedent for many tunnels that were to follow. It was not the first tunnel to be mechanically ventilated nor the first tunnel to be driven through Hudson River silt, and it was far from being the first underriver highway. But it does have the outstanding distinction of being the first long tunnel specially planned for heavy motor traffic, and it was equipped with a ventilation system representing a marked advance over any previous one. The history of this tunnel goes back somewhat farther than the days of the automobile age, for it began with projects to bridge the Hudson. As time passed, better facilities for crossing the Hudson became more urgently needed at New York. Private enterprise having failed to accomplish the construction of new facilities, the project was taken up by the states of New York and New Jersey through two commissions appointed, one by each state, for the specific purpose of investigating the

184

feasibility of a highway bridge. The Commissions' studies having showed that a downtown location favored a tunnel rather than a bridge, the two states authorized its construction in 1919 and agreed to finance the project as a joint state venture to be operated as a toll crossing upon a self-sustaining basis. Clifford M. Holland, after whom the tunnel was subsequently named, was appointed Chief Engineer and, by the beginning of 1920, had completed his tentative plans. By this time the automobile was cutting an important figure in New York traffic, and Holland realized that no vehicular tunnel could be operated successfully under a river as wide as the Hudson unless its ventilation system was designed for extremely heavy motor-vehicle traffic.

*Exhaust Gases Become a Problem.*

This brought an entirely novel problem, for the exhaust of automobile engines contains a goodly proportion of carbon monoxide, a colorless and odorless gas which can become very dangerous to life if persons are exposed to it in confined quarters. The gravity of this risk is shown by the frequency with which monoxide poisoning results from running engines of cars in small closed garages. It was necessary for Holland to begin his ventilation studies with the automobiles themselves. He had first to find how much of this gas was released by the average car under operating conditions before he could design his ventilation system. So a very comprehensive program of investigation was begun. Cars and trucks were tested under road conditions and also in closed chambers, while the volume and proportions of the exhaust gases were carefully measured. Next, there had to be found the exact effect of this gas upon persons exposed to it. Hence, in other test chambers, volunteer subjects were deliberately subjected to the effects of this gas in varying percentages and for varying periods of time. By the time this research work was completed, the engineers were able to design a system that would maintain the tunnel atmosphere at a standard of purity better than is found in the open air of some heavily traveled city streets.

This surprising result was accomplished by the unusual and original method adopted for circulating air through the tunnel. Instead of blowing air into the tunnel at its end or at intermediate shafts as with all earlier ventilation systems, Holland's staff (under the direction of Ole Singstad who later became Chief Engineer) devised what has since become known as the "vertical transverse flow" system. Fresh air drawn in through louvers in the sides of the ventilation buildings is forced through large air ducts below the tunnel floor. From these it is led, through flues spaced a short distance apart throughout the tunnel, into expansion chambers that run the full length of the tunnel and are placed at each side of the roadway slightly above the curb level. Out of these continuous chambers the air issues as a gentle stream, although in the duct below the floor it may have the velocity of a hurricane. Mixing with the exhaust gases of passing cars, it floats upwards towards the ceiling and is sucked, through grilled openings, into the exhaust air duct above. Once in this duct it is drawn by powerful suction fans to the ventilation buildings and thence discharged upwards through openings in their roofs. As a result of this system, there is neither any appreciable wind in the tunnel nor is there any noticeable odor to signify the presence of some of the more noisome (although really less dangerous) of the exhaust gases

## The Tunnel Is Begun.

Construction of this tunnel began with the breaking of ground on Canal Street, New York, on October 12, 1920. From then, the work progressed rapidly, and in a comparatively short time as many as five shields were at work at one time on the two underriver tubes and the various underground sections connecting with them. The usual array of troubles was encountered, including occasional serious "blows" when the silt cover above one or another of the river shields suddenly gave way, compressed air blowing out in front of the shield and allowing water and mud to flow into the heading. The uncertainties of this work kept the engineering staff on its toes, and Holland—a man who took his responsibilities very seriously—was soon devoting every hour of his time to the job, sacrificing sleep and proper care of his health whenever he felt that exigencies of the work demanded it. Finally, his health gave way and he was forced to take a rest in an effort to recuperate. But, unfortunately, it had been delayed too long, and on October 27, 1924, he passed away—by the irony of fate just two days before the first of the twin tubes was holed through under the river. From that time on, the "Hudson River Vehicular Tunnel" began to lose its rather unwieldy caption in favor of the shorter title of "Holland Tunnel"—a title which was given official recognition by the joint Commissions the month after Holland's death. Milton H. Freeman, Holland's Engineer of Construction, took up the mantle of responsibility upon the death of his chief but in March of the next year he, also, fell a victim of overwork, and the lot of carrying the work on now fell to Ole Singstad, Holland's Engineer of Design, who then carried the tunnel through to completion and took charge of its initial operation.

*Finished and Opened in 1927.*

The Holland Tunnel was officially dedicated on November 12, 1927. Following a procession of official cars, the tubes were thrown open for public inspection, and about 20,000 persons took advantage of this, their first and last, opportunity to walk through the tunnel. At 7 P.M. the tubes were closed permanently to pedestrian traffic and at one minute after midnight were thrown open to motor traffic exclusively, some drivers having waited in line for hours to be among the first making the passage. The tunnel became an immediate and outstanding success, and by 1931 its annual traffic was nearing the 13,000,000 mark. As an engineering project it was equally successful, as we may judge from the extent to which its distinctive and original features have been copied in tunnels subsequently built or now under construction. Although spoken of as the Holland Tunnel, it really consists of two separate tubes, one for eastbound and one for westbound traffic and spaced about fifty-nine feet apart between their centers under mid-river. From portal to portal these tubes average 8,463 feet in length, of which distance 5,480 feet lies beneath the river. All the river portions and nearly all the rest were built by the use of tunneling shields, these sections consisting of iron shells twenty-nine and a half feet outside and lined inside with concrete. The roadway is twenty feet wide; the tunnel headroom is about thirteen and a half feet. Under mid-river, the top of each tube is about seventy-two feet below mean high water and about sixteen feet under the river bottom. The total cost of the entire project was slightly over $48,000,000 this sum being supplied by the two states and refunded to them by The Port of New York Authority after this body took over operation of the tunnel in 1930.

Throughout its entire length from plaza to plaza, traffic is controlled by a very complete and thoroughly efficient signal system. At intervals of about 240 feet along one wall of each tube are signal units which can be

189

made to show green or red. Normally all of these lights are green, but, if traffic should be interrupted for any reason, they can be changed to red from any point of traffic interruption back to the tube entrance. Beyond the interruption point all others remain green, thus allowing unobstructed traffic to proceed on its way. Besides these lights are signals reading "Stop Engine," which are brought into use only in case of an extended tieup. At one side of the traffic lane is a raised walkway patrolled by uniformed tunnel police who maintain contact with the traffic supervisor by means of telephones. On the top floor of the New York administration building on Canal Street is located the Supervisor's room which forms the "nerve center" of the tunnel-operating system. From this central point one man can, if necessary, direct the entire operation of the ventilation system and movement of the tunnel traffic. By means of an elaborate system of tunnel telephones, he is able to keep in direct communication with the patrolmen stationed along the walkways in the twin tubes, and, by remote-control apparatus, he can start or stop any of the large ventilating fans.

*The Ventilating Equipment.*

To provide adequate ventilation for the Holland Tunnel there are four great buildings, two on each side of the river, housing a total of forty-two enormous blowers and forty-two equally huge exhausters—of which about two-thirds are required for capacity operation, the rest being available as reserve for emergencies. When operating at maximum capacity, the total amount of air pumped into this tunnel is about 3,761,000 cubic feet per minute. This volume may be easier to visualize if we consider its weight. The average man usually thinks of air as having little or no weight and we speak of things being "as light as air." Yet to supply this much the big fans have to handle 150 *tons of air per minute!* To ensure reliability, the electric supply for operation of these fans is drawn from six separate sources, three on each side of the river, and the system is so connected that any one of the six sources can be used to supply any or all fans. Yet, even if serious difficulty necessitated shutting down of a substantial portion of this ventilation system, the tunnel could be safely continued in operation. About the very worst result would be a slight odor of exhaust gas—not enough to warrant suspending operations.

*Oakland-Alameda Tunnel.*

Following the Holland Tunnel there came a series of more or less similar tunnels in various parts of the United States and Europe. First of these was the George A. Posey Tube, connecting Oakland with Alameda, California, and named after the county engineer who first proposed building it some years ago. This is a single-tube tunnel, carrying two-way traffic and very closely resembling the Holland. Construction was begun in May of 1925, and it was opened to traffic

191

in October of 1928. Whereas most of the Holland Tunnel was built by shield methods, the underwater portion of the Posey was constructed by the "trench system" and the rest within cofferdams. For the underwater part, twelve cylindrical sections, each 203 feet long and weighing about 5,000 tons, were constructed of steel plates upon a steel frame. This work was done in a dockyard about six miles from the site and the sections were launched like ships, floated to the site and, one by one, were sunk into position into a trench which had been dredged across the bottom of Oakland Estuary. Adjacent segments were then coupled together by divers working under the water, after which the joints were sealed, the top of the tube covered over and all water pumped out of the interior. The inside was then concreted and completed without any need for compressed air.

The underground ends connecting with the underwater tube were built by cut-and-cover subway methods, and, while one of these sections was being built, a most unexpected problem arose. To provide a base, the engineers first laid the usual foundation "mat" of concrete at the bottom of the excavation, and upon this they spread waterproofing compound to keep the finished tube dry. Upon this waterproofing, they next proceeded to lay the concrete that would form the floor of the subway. After a considerable stretch of this concrete had been placed, the unexpected difficulty arose. The heat generated by the chemical action of the setting

Fig. 36.—Ribbons of river-bed silt oozing through two open doors of a shield used in building the Holland Tunnel. With the great pressure of powerful hydraulic jacks forcing this shield ahead, the silt flows through its open doors just like toothpaste coming out of a squeezed tube. (*Courtesy of The Port of New York Authority.*)

Fig. 37.—Building the Second Cascade Tunnel. This view was taken in the "pioneer" bore which was cut parallel to the main tunnel to facilitate the work. At the left is shown a cross-cut tunnel connecting with the main one. (*Courtesy of Great Northern Railway.*)

(Facing page 199)

FIG. 38.—Excavating for the Lacroze Subway at Buenos Aires where the soil was so firm that it was scooped out to full depth by a power shovel, the sides standing without bracing or shoring until the concrete walls were built. (*Courtesy of United Engineers & Constructors, Inc.*)

concrete softened the waterproofing. Now, in an ordinary case this would have had no effect upon construction, but it happened that the subway was, necessarily, built on a down grade of slightly over four and a half per cent—and thereby hangs a tale. For the entire mass of partially completed construction began to slide downhill towards the river as one unit, the softened waterproofing serving to provide a nicely lubricated slide! Fortunately, the movement was noticed as soon as it began, and frantic efforts were made to stop the big slide. But, by the time jacks could be set in place and the great mass stopped, the whole work had moved about six inches. Luckily this was not enough to cause serious harm and the rest of the job went on without further trouble.

*Detroit-Windsor and Antwerp Tunnels.*

Next came the Detroit-Windsor tunnel, another highway tunnel, which runs under the Detroit River at the city of the same name and connects with Windsor, Ontario. The river part of this tunnel also was built by the "trench system," the method being somewhat similar to that used for the Posey, except that a concrete casing was first applied to the exterior of the sections before they were sunk. Construction began in 1928 and was completed in 1930, the total cost of this entire project being about $25,000,000. By this time it was beginning to appear as if the building of highway tunnels had become an epidemic. Even before the

Detroit Tunnel had been started there was another under way. This was the "Queensway," of which we shall say more later, as, differing greatly from the "Holland Pattern," it warrants separate description. Before completion of the Detroit tube still another was begun in 1931 to run under the Scheldt River at Antwerp, Belgium. This Antwerp project actually included two tunnels; one a single-tube thirty-one-foot highway tunnel; the other a fifteen-and-a-half-foot pedestrian tunnel located about half a mile away from the highway tunnel but also passing under the Scheldt. Both tunnels were built by the use of shields and are formed by shells of cast-iron segments lined with concrete. Owing to the particular soil conditions under the river bed, it was decided to place the tunnels low enough to run through an impervious clay that underlies the soft mud bottom. Hence the Antwerp tunnel is (for a shield tunnel through soft ground) unusually far below the surface, the roadway being 116 feet below mean high water. This is about fourteen feet lower than the roadway of the Holland, although the Hudson River is actually deeper than the Scheldt. The Antwerp vehicular tunnel is about 5,801 feet long from portal to portal, and the pedestrian tunnel is about 1,750 feet long.

What was probably the most interesting part of this construction was the building of shafts for each of the Antwerp tunnels by means of the ground-freezing process. Walls of the ice formed by freezing the wet ground were used to protect the shaft excavations. The freezing plan is quite old, having been originated many years ago, but this was its first use in a large-diameter shaft. Six-inch pipes were sunk in the soil around the shaft excavation to form a ring about 100 feet in diameter. Smaller pipes, two inches in size, were placed within the larger ones and refrigerated brine was circulated down the smaller pipes and back up through the outer ones until the adjacent soil was solidly frozen to form a ring of ice about ten to fifteen feet thick. The center core of still-soft earth was then excavated and the concrete shaft walls placed, while the ice wall, in the meantime, served as a protective shell to hold back the ground water during the progress of this work.

*More Highway Tunnels.*

Next came the Boston Traffic Tube, built by the City of Boston in 1931–1934 to provide a roadway connection, under the harbor, which would link Boston with East Boston. Before this had been completed, still another tunnel was begun: The Port of New York Authority's Lincoln Tunnel connecting New York City with Weehawken, New Jersey. Work began in October of 1933 on the first, or south tube, and its builders attained a record by constructing 1,040 feet of the underriver section in twenty-five working days with a single shield, thus providing a startling comparison with the painfully slow progress of tunneling only a few decades earlier. Work on the second tube of this tunnel began late in 1936 and is to be finished about 1940–1941. In the meantime, the first tube will be put into operation and will carry two-way traffic until the second is ready. Owing to its large traffic capacity, its length and the high cost of real estate required for approaches, this will be one of the most expensive shield tunnels ever constructed. By the time it is completed, the cost will reach about $75,000,000, even without the $10,000,000 depressed highway which is being constructed across the Palisades.

As if to prove conclusively that we are having an "epidemic" of highway tunnels under rivers, we find that, as these words are being written, there is still another in progress: the New York City Tunnel Authority's Queens Midtown Tunnel. The New York approach of this tunnel begins at East Thirty-sixth Street and swings north nearly to Forty-second Street, from which point a pair of tubes will run under the East River to Long Island City. Work began towards the close of 1936 and the completed tunnel is expected to be in operation in 1940. Still another tunnel is to be constructed, beneath some crosstown streets in Manhattan, to link this Queens Midtown Tunnel with the Port Authority's Lincoln Tunnel. When all three are in operation, it will be possible to drive right through from New Jersey to Long Island without becoming entangled in New York's traffic and without coming up to the surface on the way.

196

*Tunnel-building Superstitions.*

Most of the adventure has been taken out of tunneling and these newer shield tunnels go through to completion without much event. But a few of the old-time superstitions still remain. One of them is the idea that bars all women from the compressed air; only in very rare cases has this rule been violated. For the sight of a woman entering the compressed-air section would be taken as foreboding an accident—yet no tunnel man can explain why or where this originated! Another old tunnel-builders' superstition, although one that is slowly dying out, is the belief that Friday is a "bad day" for the first "shove" or first forward movement of a new shield. While visiting a recent tunnel to see the shield at work, the author took advantage of this occasion to ask the "shield boss" what he thought of this bad-luck omen. But the "boss" curled his lip in contempt for superstitious tunnel workers as he answered: "*Any* day is a good day for the first shove."

## Chapter XX

# Some Western Tunnels

*Old Railroad History.*

FEW other tunnels, if any, can show a history more varied than that of the old "Busk-Ivanhoe," which is now the "Carlton" highway tunnel. The story of the Busk-Ivanhoe began around 1889–1890, when the old Colorado Midland Railway trains still wound their way upwards over the then-famous Midland Loop, a section of track that doubled back upon itself twice before finally heading into the 2,200-foot Hagerman Tunnel, which was built in 1886–1887, 11,530 feet up, through Sugar Loaf Mountain, of the Continental Divide, west of Leadville, Colorado. To eliminate part of the climb up to this original tunnel under the Divide, the Colorado Midland organized the separate but affiliated Busk Tunnel Company to cut the 9,395-foot Busk-Ivanhoe Tunnel through the mountain at an elevation of 10,800 feet above sea level. This work it completed in October of 1893, after slightly more than three years' work that cost about $1,000,000 in money and the lives of twenty men. Use of the earlier and higher tunnel was discontinued upon completion of the newer one, and trains were operated through the Busk-Ivanhoe under a 999-year lease between the tunnel company and the railroad. All went well for a time, but some important changes took place in the railroad map of that part of the country, with the result that the Midland found much of its traffic being diverted to rival lines, and it eventually landed in the hands of a receiver. The railroad property was sold under foreclosure proceedings and a new company organized to continue operation of the line. The management of the new company soon decided that the tunnel lease constituted a great hardship and made an attempt to obtain better terms from the tunnel company, which had not been involved in the receivership.

## A Tunnel "for Sale or Rent."

Being unable to effect any basis of settlement, the railroad discontinued use of the Busk Tunnel in 1898, broadcast the scenic advantages of the old route and resumed operation of its trains over the famous loop and through the Hagerman Tunnel—leaving the Busk Tunnel Company in the position of having a "tunnel for sale or to let and no customers in sight," as the *Engineering News* very aptly put it in the issue of October 6, 1898. Relieved of the expensive lease in addition to having reduced its interest charges through reorganization, the outlook for the railroad became more promising, but, in the winter of 1898–1899, the use of this higher route resulted in its line being snow-

199

bound for nearly three months. After this interruption, the two companies came to terms, use of the Busk-Ivanhoe was resumed and in the summer of 1899 it was sold to the railroad company. Until 1918 its trains continued to use the Busk-Ivanhoe Tunnel although, in the meantime, the financial affairs of the company underwent many changes and suddenly it found itself under the control of its "hated rival," the Denver and Rio Grande Railroad. The net outcome of this change was more loss of traffic and, sometime later, another bankruptcy for the Midland. In 1917 the tunnel and railroad were sold at auction to A. E. Carlton, a local business man who—at the time of making the purchase —had planned to extend the road through to Salt Lake City. However, the entry of the United States into the World War completely upset his plans and in August of 1918 the last train rolled through the two-mile tunnel. A few years later the tracks were removed and most of the right-of-way was donated to the Highway Department of the State of Colorado for the construction of a public highway. The tunnel was paved and put into use as a highway for vehicles, originally under the direction of the State Highways Engineer and, later, as a toll tunnel under the direction of its owner, Mr. Carlton. So the tunnel that began its existence by carrying the old Colorado Midland trains under the Great Divide is now the Carlton Tunnel, a short-cut highway through the heart of the Rockies, about two miles up in the air.

*More Plans for Tunneling the Divide.*

The idea of boring a tunnel through the Continental Divide west of Denver was originally planned by David Moffat, builder of the Denver, Northwestern and Pacific Railroad, to provide a direct route from Denver to the Pacific. Because it meant about six miles of expensive drilling through hard rock and a correspondingly great financial burden, nothing came of it for many years—the idea remaining just a dream of this pioneer railroad builder. As a matter of fact, Moffat died penniless in 1911 while still trying to raise funds to complete his railroad to Salt Lake and the work remained—stopped by want of money—with the tracks reaching only to Craig, Colorado, 232 miles from Denver or about half the distance to Salt Lake. As the years passed, changes took place in the railroad situation and the Denver and Salt Lake Railroad revived the idea in 1913 with a plan to build this tunnel in partnership with the City of Denver. Under this joint arrangement, the city would use the tunnel for a water-supply conduit while the railroad used it also for its tracks. This new plan obtained serious consideration and, in May of 1913, Denver appointed a Tunnel Commission to cooperate with the railroad. In February of the next year the city voters approved a bond issue to provide the city's share of the total cost, then estimated at $4,420,000. Just when it began to look as though everything was going along smoothly, legal objections were raised by opponents of the scheme

201

THE STORY OF TUNNELS

and the Colorado Supreme Court declared this bond issue unconstitutional on account of certain terms of the agreement between the railroad and the city.

*Moffat Tunnel Construction Begins.*

About nine years of bickering followed and it was the middle of 1923 before any constructive progress could be reported. In that year, the Moffat Tunnel Commission floated a $6,720,000 bond issue to finance the construction, retained J. Vipond Davies of New York as its consulting engineer, and awarded the construction contract to Hitchcock and Tinkler at a price of $5,250,-000, upon terms calling for completion of the work in forty-six months. Under the arrangement which had finally been worked out, the tunnel was to be constructed as a public work to improve the railway system of the state and would be leased to a railroad for operation upon its completion. The construction method adopted provided for driving by means of the "parallel tunnel" system as used in building the Simplon. A pilot tunnel was to be drilled at one side of the main tunnel and, after completion of all work, this pilot tunnel would be used by the City of Denver to carry a supply conduit forming part of the city water system. The finished main tunnel was to be a fraction over six miles long, sixteen feet wide and twenty-four feet high. Work started promptly after award of the contract and the tunnel builders were soon reporting excellent progress; indeed, in May of 1925, they reported 771 feet of

advance for the east heading in one fifteen-day period—
probably a record for fast tunneling in rock.

With the summit of James Peak towering about 4,000
feet above the tunnel, one might well have expected
the builders to have some trouble with water, such as
accompanied most other attempts to cut tunnels under
high mountains. These difficulties got well under way
by February of 1926, with the work about three-
quarters completed; a large underground water course
was reached on the night of the 28th, with the result
that water came into the main heading of the east end
at the rate of 3,000 gallons a minute. For two days this
continued, when the flow dropped to 1,500 gallons. It
continued at the reduced rate for thirty days and then
dropped to 1,000 gallons per minute, when drill holes
in the parallel tunnel also struck water which began
coming in there at the rate of 650 gallons per minute. It
must have seemed as though the main troubles of its
builders were being crowded into this last quarter of the
Moffat Tunnel for, in July of 1926, six men were
crushed to death under tons of rock when a portion
of the roof dropped on them just as they were bracing
it to prevent such an accident. Later progress reports
said less about difficulties, indicating that the worst
section had been passed and early on Saturday, February 12, 1927, the two opposite headings of the parallel
or water tunnel were connected by driving a thirty-
three-foot steel drill through the remaining rock
barrier. Excavation continued as before until there

remained only about eight feet separating the headings, whereupon arrangements were made to stage an appropriate ceremony. On February 18, this last eight feet of rock was blown out with a blast fired telegraphically by President Coolidge. The main headings were holed through in July and the last excavation was completed by December of 1927.

### Twelve Minutes as against Seven Hours!

The first train ran through the tunnel on February 26, 1928, carrying about 2,500 citizens of Colorado and Utah and making the trip in twelve minutes as against the seven hours required by the former route over Corona Pass. Actually, the line was shortened by only twenty-three miles, the great improvement in removing heavy grades serving to decrease time out of proportion to the distance saved. While David Moffat had planned extending his railroad to Salt Lake when he first proposed this tunnel, the question of finance again prevented the road from carrying through his plan after the tunnel had been completed. As it was of little value without a western connection, the best alternative seemed to be that of constructing a forty-mile cutoff running from the western end of the tunnel to meet the Denver and Rio Grande Western Railroad at Dotsero. But, even this relatively moderate expense was beyond the ability of the Denver and Salt Lake to finance— hence the whole future of the tunnel was again "up in the air." About this time the Tunnel Commission also found itself with a new trouble on its hands. The unexpected rock conditions had brought about increased construction costs and, to finance these, the Commissioners issued more bonds when the need for funds arose. In July of 1928, some Colorado taxpayers brought suit against the Commission demanding cancellation of the entire bond issue, claiming that the Commissioners should have gone to the voters for authority to issue the new series. This point, however, was settled a few months later when the courts decided that the bonds were valid and that the Commission had full power to issue the additional amount without recourse to the voters for authority. At the same time this decision did not end the Commission's worries on the score of greater cost; in February of 1929, the Denver and Salt Lake Railroad raised objection to paying a rental based upon the increased cost of the tunnel. The road claimed that its agreement of lease covered only its share of the carrying charges in accordance with the *original estimate* of cost. To convince the Commission that it meant business, the road even threatened to revert to using its old route over the pass if the extra rental was insisted upon. This point also was settled in favor of the Commission, in the face of which decision the road decided to continue using the tunnel.

Around 1932, events took a new turn when the Denver and Rio Grande Western Railroad obtained control of the old "Moffat Road," as it was often called. Plans were then made to connect the Denver and Salt Lake with its own lines by construction of the much-discussed cutoff from the Moffat line west of the tunnel to meet the Denver and Rio Grande at Dotsero. So, at last, David Moffat's dream of carrying his road through to Salt Lake was to be realized, although not until many years after his death. Starting in June of 1934, the tunnel began to be used jointly by the Chicago, Burlington and Quincy Railroad and the Denver and Rio Grande Western Railroad; on June 16th, trains passing through it were routed over the completed Dotsero Cutoff.

*The Two Cascade Tunnels.*

While the Moffat Tunnel was nearing completion in Colorado, another epoch-making railroad tunnel was begun in the northwestern corner of the United States. This was the Great Northern Railway's New Cascade Tunnel, the third of its series of Cascade Mountain crossings at this point. Its original route crossed Stevens Pass by means of a switchback railroad with heavy grades, completed in 1892 and operated until 1900. This route was abandoned after completion of its first Cascade Tunnel, a two-and-a-half-mile bore under Stevens Pass, which saved considerable heavy grades as well as mileage and also served to greatly reduce interruption of operations by snow in wintertime. As the road's traffic grew, still further improvement of its Cascades crossing became desirable, and in 1925 it

206

began construction of a second Cascade Tunnel at a considerably lower level than the first. This new tunnel was to be slightly more than three times the length of the first and was planned to eliminate more of the heavy grades, permitting faster operation of still heavier trains. In addition, the lower level would further reduce trouble with snow, which had forced the construction of eight miles of snow sheds and was costing $600,000 a year to remove from the tracks. The original Cascade Tunnel was operated by steam locomotives until 1909, when the tunnel was electrified.

During the period of steam operation, considerable trouble was encountered when attempting to pull heavy trains over the long grades. Indeed, "helping" engines had often to be used. In February of 1903, smoke in this first Cascade Tunnel nearly caused the death of a train crew and passengers when they became stalled in the tunnel. The trouble arose when an eastbound passenger train hooked on a large freight engine to help pull it through the tunnel. The coupling between the two engines began giving trouble even before the tunnel was reached, and it pulled out three times in the tunnel. On each occasion it was repaired and the train again started. As a result of this long delay, with two engines belching forth smoke at each start, the tunnel air became filled with a suffocating smoke, whereupon the train crew decided to send the freight engine ahead for help. Shortly after it left, the conductor realized that the tunnel air was becoming dangerously filled with smoke and that the train should be backed out. He went ahead to the locomotive only to find the engineer and fireman already unconscious and he, also, was overcome before he could release the brakes. Sensing trouble, the brakeman followed him but was also overcome. Rather fortunately for all concerned, one of the road's firemen, by the name of Abbot, happened to be a passenger on the train and realized that something was seriously wrong. Alarmed by the condition of the air which was growing worse by the minute, he took it upon himself to act and, struggling through the choking smoke, fought his way forward to the locomotive cab where the entire train crew lay unconscious. Releasing the air brakes, he allowed the train to roll backwards down the grade until it was out of the tunnel. Again rather fortunately, he managed to retain consciousness and was able to stop the train as it emerged from the tunnel, thus saving all from another accident. Most of the passengers had become seriously affected by the smoke by this time, several were unconscious and three of the train crew had to be given hospital treatment, but all recovered. With electrification of the tunnel completed in 1909, steam locomotives were no longer operated through it and all danger of a repetition of this incident was thus removed. The second Cascade Tunnel is not only electrically operated but its design provides natural ventilation and there is always a strong current of fresh air blowing through it.

Fig. 39.—Digging a sewer tunnel through the stiff blue clay under Chicago's streets. Two men cut off the clay in strips by means of a drawknife while a third man catches each strip and passes it back to a little car on which excavated material is transported to the shaft. After being cut to the required size, the hole is lined inside with concrete. (*Courtesy of Engineering News-Record.*)

Fig. 40.—Adjusting a conveyor used to carry lumps of silt away from the shield when building the Lincoln Tunnel. (*Courtesy of The Port of New York Authority.*)

Fig. 41.—Part of the mechanism of a shield used in building the Holland Tunnel. The large device in the foreground is an erector which lifts the iron segments; toward the right may be seen some of the hydraulic jacks that were used to push this shield through the silt.

Fig. 42.—A power shovel at work under the Hudson River! Silt which was taken in through the shield and deposited in the bottom of the Lincoln Tunnel is being removed in preparation for installation of the concrete lining. (*Photographs courtesy of The Port of New York Authority.*)

*The Second Cascade Tunnel.*

It must have taken a lot of courage on the part of the Great Northern to undertake construction of its new Cascade Tunnel, for it already had the original Cascade Tunnel in use. In addition, an energetic group of promoters was actively campaigning for a gigantic undertaking: the construction of a thirty-mile tunnel under the Cascades, for a highway, to be built with state and national funds on the basis of a virtual subsidy. This venture, would, of course, be in direct competition with the Great Northern's proposed new tunnel as well as its original one. But the railroad evidently felt sure that nothing tangible would come of the proposal for, right in the middle of this agitation, it suddenly announced its award of a contract for the construction of a new Cascade Tunnel. This new tunnel was to be seven and three-quarter miles long and would thus become the longest railroad tunnel in America. Work began on December 14, 1925, and was soon making outstanding progress. Indeed, it was not long before claims were being laid to some tunneling speed records. This was despite the water troubles which always seem to accompany the drilling of long tunnels under high mountains, the incoming water in the New Cascade Tunnel reaching a maximum of 10,000 gallons per minute at one stage. The temperature of this water reached a maximum of seventy degrees Fahrenheit at the deepest point, which was rather a pleasant surprise, since as much as 100 degrees had really been expected. The new tunnel was holed through on May 1, 1928, with a blast fired by President Coolidge over the telegraph wires from Washington, D. C., and in just about three years from the start of its construction, the long bore was finished. The first train pulled through it on January 12, 1929, with appropriate dedication ceremonies as the longest railway tunnel in America was officially declared open.

## Chapter XXI

# Queensway—The Largest Underwater Tunnel

---

*Some Distinctive Features.*

THE Mersey River Highway Tunnel, constructed jointly by Liverpool and Birkenhead to connect these two cities, runs under the Mersey just one city block away from the famous old railroad tunnel of 1885. This new tunnel has many features of interest. To start with, it is the largest-diameter tunnel ever bored under a river, and its construction required the largest tunneling shield that has ever been used. Then, too, its whole arrangement differs greatly from that of other modern roadway tunnels. It is constructed mainly of a shell of cast-iron segmental rings resembling other shield-tunnel construction, except that it measures forty-six and a quarter feet as against (for example) the thirty-one-foot diameter of the new Lincoln Tunnel at New York. All the Mersey Tunnel construction, including both the underground and the underriver portions, was cut through sandstone rock; although shields were used in building it, no part of this tunnel runs through river-

211

bed silt. The greater depth of the "Queensway"—
as the tunnel has been officially named—resulted from
two things: one was the greater depth of the Mersey
as against that of many other rivers under which tunnels
have been built; the other was the large diameter of
the tunnel itself. Combined, these two factors inspired
the engineers' decision to carry their construction low
enough to keep all of it in solid rock under the river.
As a result, the lowest point of the tunnel roadway is
148 feet below the river, or about the height of a four-
teen-story building, as compared with ninety-three feet
for the Holland and 116 feet for the Antwerp tunnel.

Although its cast-iron shell is similar, the inside
arrangement of this tunnel is entirely different from
those of the "Holland pattern." Since the single large
tube of the Queensway serves to carry two-way traffic,
its main roadway is thirty-six feet wide, almost one
and three-quarter times that of the Holland Tunnel
roadways. Its paving is unusual; with the exception
of a short rubber-block stretch near the Birkenhead
end, all paving is of diamond-tread, *cast-iron blocks.*
The ventilation system is also different from that of
most highway tunnels, except that it embodies the
Holland feature of supplying fresh air through diffusion
slots running the length of the tunnel and on each side
of the roadway. Here, however, the comparison ends.
In the Queensway, the fresh air is carried through *two*
ducts under the roadway instead of through a single
one occupying the entire space below. Between these

two ducts there is a large space, which may, later, be used as an additional tube for future traffic. Although not actually cut off by a ceiling as in tunnels of the Holland type, the upper portion of the arch is similarly used for carrying the vitiated air to the shafts. As the air comes into the roadway tube from the diffusing slots, it mixes with the exhaust gases, floats upward to the high arched ceiling and thence toward the ventilation shafts, through which it is drawn up into the ventilation buildings and exhausted into the outer air through the building roof—this last feature being one of the few that resemble those of the "Holland-type" ventilation buildings.

### More Construction Details.

The Queensway has six ventilation buildings, three on each side of the river, and all of them differ considerably in arrangement from those of the "Holland pattern." Probably the chief point of distinction is in the fact that fresh air is drawn in *through the roof* of each building instead of through louvers in its sides, an arrangement adopted with the object of eliminating annoyance to occupants of adjoining buildings by the noise of powerful ventilating machinery. This equipment, including reserve machinery which is available for emergencies, required a total of thirty fans of immense proportions. Indeed, the largest single fan has a capacity of 641,000 cubic feet of air, or nearly twenty-six tons, per minute. Its casing measures fifty feet across and it towers above the floor to about the height of a three-story building. The traffic-control equipment, signals, fire alarms and other operating equipment of the Queensway differ somewhat in appearance and design from those of the Holland type of tunnels, although their functions are generally similar.

The length of this tunnel, from portal to portal of the main section, is 10,584 feet, or about one quarter longer than the Holland. In addition to this main tunnel, however, there are also two branches, one at each end leading up to the water front with nineteen-foot roadways for two-way traffic. The greater length of the tunnel as compared with the Holland is due to its greater depth, for the Mersey at this point is only 3,784 feet as against the 5,500-foot width of the Hudson where the Holland Tunnel passes under it. One result of eliminating the overhead air duct is to greatly increase the headroom at least so far as appearance is concerned. Hence the Mersey tunnel has headroom of twenty-three feet as compared with thirteen and a half feet for the Holland and about the same for other tunnels of this type. Headroom in the branches is not quite so great, the minimum being seventeen feet. Since the open-ceiling arch serves as an air duct, vehicles over thirteen feet high are not allowed to use the tunnel.

*Cement Grouting Solves Water Problems.*

Considerable trouble was encountered with water during construction of the Queensway, but cement grouting prevented this from assuming the serious aspect that it did in earlier days of tunneling. Because of the great depth, the use of air pressure was barred from consideration, for it would have taken seventy-three and a half pounds to the square inch to balance the water pressure at the depth of about 170 feet reached by the tunnel at its lowest point. This, of course, is considerably beyond the generally accepted safe limit of fifty pounds for compressed-air workers. To relieve the difficulty, pilot tunnels were used during construction; one being in the upper part and one in the lower part of the main tunnel heading. These were kept somewhat in advance of the main tunnel shield, and extensive pumping of cement grout from the pilot tunnels was resorted to in efforts to close rock seams and thus decrease the amount of incoming water. From the Liverpool side a drainage tunnel was also driven out for some distance below the main tunnel and was connected with it by means of drill holes and shafts. Despite the extensive grouting, so much water came in during the progress of the construction work that the total amount pumped out equalled about twenty-six times the weight of rock that was excavated! Once the cast-iron shell had been placed and caulked that, of course, put an end to the incoming water.

Construction of this tunnel was directed by Sir Basil Mott, an engineer of long experience whose record dates back as far as association with Greathead on the

City and South London Railway tunnels and with Sir Benjamin Baker on construction of the Central London Railway. Work began in December of 1925, and the tunnel was opened in July of 1934, although some of the ventilation buildings were not fully completed until the following year. In round figures the total cost of the project was about $40,000,000 and its construction required the excavation of about 1,200,000 tons of rock. About 82,000 tons of cast iron were required for the rings forming its great shell. But nothing illustrates the size of this undertaking quite so well as the vast amount of explosives that were used. For blasting the rock took 560,000 pounds—enough to conduct a war of considerable importance had their energy been directed in this more destructive manner.

# Chapter XXII
# Moscow Builds a Subway

*With Marble-faced Columns and Walls.*

To THE average American it may come as quite a surprise to learn that one of the most palatial subways in the world was recently completed by the Soviet Government in its capital city of Moscow. The photographs of its marble-faced columns and walls, its strikingly beautiful lighting fixtures and the paneled ceilings of its underground stations provide ample evidence that the Soviet publications are not overstating a fact when they proudly announce that "The Moscow subway is the best in the world." Plans for a Moscow subway were first considered as early as 1902, long before the World War, the Russian revolution and the radical changes that followed these events. None of the earlier plans went beyond the stage of talk, and it was not until very recently—June of 1931 to be exact—that construction of the first parts of a comprehensive system was definitely decided upon. Ground was broken in November of 1931, but no substantial progress was made for about a year and a half; only something like ten per cent of the initial unit of the system was built by the end of 1933.

This rate of progress was far from the liking of Lazar M. Kaganovich, Commissar of Railways, and a radical change in the rate of progress was ordered at the close of the year. Excavation was to be five times as fast, concreting was to be eight to nine times as fast as it had been in the year then closing. Thousands of volunteer workers were organized into brigades to speed up the work, and there began a drive to increase the rate of progress. Schedules and quotas were assigned which would have been considered impossible of attainment in most other countries. Speed became a slogan and a fetish, just as it did with the first "Five-year Plan" which was then drawing to a close. Working with that unity of purpose and enthusiasm that only wartime conditions can arouse in other countries, the Russians began to accomplish amazing results. Workers reached the incredible total of 75,000 at the peak; bonuses were paid for extra work, and construction spurted suddenly upwards. Within ten months, trial runs were being made over partially completed sections of the line; in still another four months the structure was complete, and, on May 15, 1935, the line was opened for regular operation. A total of about six miles of the route had been completed in the startling time of one year— a record entirely without precedent and one that is best appreciated if we consider the records made elsewhere. It took the City of New York seven or eight years to complete the first thirteen miles of its "Independent" Subway; it took Philadelphia five years to complete six miles of its Broad Street subway; it took the City of Tokyo two and a half years to build four miles of route, and probably the nearest "runner up" to Moscow was the four-and-a-half-mile extension of the Buenos Aires subway, which took about twenty-one months—even this was constructed under much more favorable conditions and by an experienced organization.

*The First Unit of a Large System.*

This first section of Moscow's subway is only the initial unit of a system that will, as now planned, eventually total something like fifty miles of routes. As it is, construction of a nine-mile extension was begun as soon as the first section went into operation. This second unit went into operation in April of 1937, whereupon a six-mile third unit was immediately begun. As the general plan of Moscow is radial, the subway system was shaped to suit this arrangement. Routes were planned to radiate from the center of the city toward the suburbs, and the first unit consists of three of these "spokes" meeting at the center of the city to form a giant Y on the map. The second section adds more great spokes to converge upon the central hub.

Construction was far from being the simple task that the startling rate of progress on the first unit might

219

lead one to expect. On the contrary, extremely adverse
conditions were encountered in many portions of the
line, and almost every known method of tunneling
had to be used before the job was completed. Test
borings showed that part of the route would cut through
sixty feet of "soupy" quicksand which filled the buried
channels of four ancient and forgotten rivers. Swelling
clay that in six weeks crumpled twenty-inch timbers
like matchsticks was encountered in other parts, and
in still others were found innumerable subterranean
passages that dated back to the days of medieval
Russia. These passages had to be explored and mapped
by a trained staff. Depths were equally varied, ranging
from shallow cut-and-cover work down to depths
like that of the Kirovskaya Station, which is 118 feet
below the ground. Construction methods were chosen
to suit the individual characteristics of the extremely
varied conditions encountered. About fifty-five per
cent of the distance was excavated by underground
mining methods; slightly less than 3,000 feet was
constructed by the use of shields; some 262 feet was
constructed by sinking pneumatic caissons and about
10,666 feet by the "Parisian" method. This consists
of digging two parallel trenches and in these building
the side walls, then excavating the street only enough
to permit constructing the roof between these walls,
after which the ground is backfilled and the street
relaid; the main part of the excavation is then continued under cover of this roof. Another twenty-five

per cent of the route was built by open-cut and cut-and-cover methods.

*Freezing and Chemical Grouting.*

In some bad ground, freezing was resorted to in order to solidify the quicksands sufficiently for working in safety. A system of "chemical" grouting, developed from a German process by the Soviet chemists and engineers, was used in other cases. This process begins with the injection of "waterglass," a liquid—known chemically as silicate of soda—which hardens to almost the consistency of stone. The silicate was followed by an injection of a solution of either calcium chloride or sodium chloride (common salt) and was sometimes used in conjunction with cement. These chemicals were injected by force pumps through one-inch pipes about fifteen to thirty feet long and perforated with small holes. The injections congealed in the quicksand, hardening it to a thickness of more than three feet in fifteen or twenty minutes. This was sufficient to prevent its oozing into the heading, and in some cases it was rendered almost as hard as common building brick. Some of the tunneling was done under normal air pressure and other parts with air pressures ranging up to thirty pounds to the square inch, but without a shield. Although used on less than 3,000 feet of the first line, the shield method appealed particularly to the Russian engineers because of their leaning toward the maximum use of machine methods. Two shields were used on this

221

unit, one imported from England and the other an all-Russian product of which the Soviet engineers felt very proud, as it was their first attempt in this field. Experience proved that, in this first Moscow subway, shield work was about seventy per cent cheaper and five or six times faster than other methods. However, this is probably due in part to the extensive use of "hand-power" methods applied elsewhere along the route—hand shovels and wheelbarrows being generally used in place of the power shovels and other mechanical devices that are used to such a large extent in America. In building the second unit, considerably greater use was made of machinery. The surprising speed with which the Moscow subway was built may be credited to good organization and to the unprecedented number of workers engaged on its construction. Official records show that the working force on the first unit averaged 65,000 and that as many as 75,000 workers were engaged upon the project when the work reached its peak of employment in May of 1934. Most of this was voluntary labor, untrained in construction and recruited from factories and elsewhere—workers who entered into the project patriotically in much the same spirit that other countries can inspire only in wartime. Except for the one tunneling shield which was imported from England, every part of the subway construction material and equipment was supplied by the Russian plants—a fact in which the Soviet Government took particular pride, since this included much intricate mechanism like automatic block signals, motors and escalators, as well as steel and cement.

*Some of the Construction Details.*

The total length of the initial unit of the Moscow "Metro," as it has been called, is slightly over seven miles; that of the second is just over nine miles. The tunnels are eighteen feet in diameter, and the tracks, like those of other Russian railways, are five-foot gauge. The first unit of the system has thirteen stations and the second has nine, all finely finished and brilliantly lighted, a lighting intensity of two to four times that used in most other subway systems being claimed. The three parallel escalators at Krasniye Vorota (Red Gate) Station are about 200 feet long and are claimed to be the longest escalators in the world. The cost of the first unit of the Moscow Metro has been figured roughly at $40,000,000 and that of the second at slightly more, as well as it is possible to make a direct cost conversion into American money. However, the extensive use of voluntary labor and other special conditions of construction render impracticable any sound basis of comparison with the cost of subways built in most other countries. In the Soviet Union, all land is the property of the state, hence the cost of right-of-way becomes a rather intangible factor although often representing an element of major importance in the costs elsewhere. Toward the end of its nicely printed descriptive booklet on the initial unit of this unusual subway, we are informed by the Russians that: "Each carriage can accomodate 170 passengers. There are seats for fifty *and standing room for* 120 *passengers.*" The italics are put there by the present writer, for the words seemed to suggest that our own subways had one thing, at least, in common with the grand new subway in Moscow!

Fig. 43.—One of the Piccadilly Tube trains at Hammersmith Station.

Fig. 44.—The "ticket hall" of Manor House Station on London's Piccadilly Tube. (*Photographs courtesy of London Passenger Transport Board.*)

FIG. 45.—Crymskaya Square, one of the marble-columned stations on Moscow's first subway.

FIG. 46.—A foreign delegation in the first station of the Moscow Subway.
(*Photographs courtesy of Intourist, Inc.*)

## Chapter XXIII

# "Unfinished Business"

The English Channel Tunnel.

THE regularity with which a big project can be alternately forgotten, revived and forgotten bears everlasting tribute to the fickle memory of the general public. About 1882 the French and the British began construction of a tunnel which was to run under the English Channel and by the following year had completed *almost two and a half miles* of their preliminary bores extending well out under the sea. Yet, today, only a few people seem to be aware of the existence of this partially completed tunnel. So far as is known, the first mention of a tunnel under the Channel was in a proposal made to Napoleon Bonaparte by a mining engineer named Mathieu. About 1838 or 1839, and again between 1851 and 1855, Thome de Gamond, a hydrographic and mining engineer and military officer, carried on considerable work of investigation, although nothing tangible came of his plans. Many other schemes followed, some eminently practical; others purely visionary. One Hector Horeau, described in the news reports as a Paris architect, advanced a proposal to lay an iron tube upon the floor of the Channel, anchoring it in place to prevent it from floating up to the surface.

Still another plan came up in 1868 when an English civil engineer, Austin by name, proposed a tunnel which was to be bored under the Channel and interrupted by a shaft constructed upon a submerged island that lies a short distance below the water in mid-channel. This was the most ambitious of all Channel tunnel schemes; it was to consist of three tubes, each about thirty feet in diameter. Despite the frequency with which Channel tunnel schemes came into public notice, little or nothing was accomplished until after the problem was taken up by the noted engineer Sir John Hawkshaw. His investigations began in 1865, following which he enlisted the financial support of the Southeastern Railway in England while the Rothschild Brothers lent their support to the French company. Marine surveys were made in 1865 and 1866 which showed that the chalk, visible in the white cliffs of Dover, continued right across the bed of the Channel to France at a depth which would make the construction of a tunnel practicable. At no point was the water more than 200 feet deep, and the location chosen was at the point where the Channel was narrowest; between Sangatte in France and Shakespeare Cliff between Dover and Folkstone in England.

*Construction Begun in 1882.*

By 1876 several thousand soundings had been made and many specimens of the bottom material had been taken. To continue this work, a Channel Tunnel Company was incorporated in England in 1872, and a corresponding company was incorporated in France in 1875. The work began with high expectations but—as it developed later—with insufficient regard for the insular spirit of the British of that day and age. Construction started with the sinking of shafts on each side of the Channel in 1882, and preparations were made to begin tunneling. The material through which the tunnel was to pass consisted of chalk mixed with clay, forming a material so impervious to water and so firm that no lining of the excavation was considered necessary in the original plans. This material, experiments showed, could be cut away almost like cheese. Yet, despite its ease of working, the chalk stood up safely without need of shoring or internal lining of the tunnel. On the whole, it promised to be an ideal material for tunneling. At the French side a shaft was sunk to a depth of 280 feet; at the English side it had to be carried down only 150 feet. A preliminary, seven-foot, tunnel was then begun to run out under the sea.

By this time, the entire world was awaking to interest in the project; even on this side of the Atlantic, publications were beginning to give it considerable notice. The whole idea of running trains under the Channel between France and England fired the imagination. But in England an active opposition arose which began to put pressure upon the government to prevent execution of the scheme. The opposing group had the support of numerous army and navy officials who had visions of the dire prospect of opening England up to invasion by way of the tunnel. Lively sessions resulted when a Joint Commission of the House of Lords and House of Commons was appointed to report upon the plan. On May 30, 1883, this Commission sent a party of its members to Dover to see the work at first hand. The whole country sat bolt upright and took an active share in the argument. On one side were forward-looking business men and engineers who favored pushing the tunnel project to completion; on the other side were many thousands who literally shivered in their boots at the very prospect of ending Britain's isolation by sea. Vainly did the tunnel advocates point out the facility with which the long bore could be flooded at first signs of trouble. Their opponents conjured wild dreams of Frenchmen pouring out in hordes from the English end of the tunnel to make the "tight little island" a mere vassal of France—all of this despite the fact that Britain and France were then on the best of terms.

*A Record That Stands to This Day.*

Even at this early stage, the engineers had accomplished enough to show that construction of the tunnel might have become an actual fact within a few years had the problems of financing and British permission been solved. The matter of financing showed every promise of solution with the powerful support of the

Rothschilds and a British and French railway behind the venture; the prospects of British permission became hopelessly bogged in the mire of invasion fears. So the work came to an end for the time being in 1883, with the English heading running out 6,200 feet from the Dover shaft and the French one extending 6,027 feet from the shaft at Sangatte. A special boring machine had been developed for cutting away the chalk and operating tests showed it to be quite practical. In fact, its ability had been demonstrated by driving a seven-foot hole through this chalk bed at the perfectly astounding rate of *sixteen feet an hour!* This is a speed which has never been equalled in submarine tunneling even to this day. The machine had a series of rotating disk knives that shaved off chalk from the face of the heading; the debris was fed into a pulverizer which quickly reduced it to a fine powder, whereupon it was mixed with water, flushed through pipes and thence conveyed to the surface. Judging by all reports, this machine must have been the answer to a tunnel-builder's prayer! However, by this time the French Channel Tunnel Company—which had been organized to cooperate with the British Company—became discouraged by the reluctance of the British Government to sanction the scheme. Hence, in March of 1883, it decided to suspend operations at Sangatte until a decision had been reached by Parliament. This decision soon followed, but the answer was "NO." The special Joint Commission of the Lords and Commons rejected the proposal as not in accord with the interests of British national security.

The Channel tunnel project, however, had already shown that it has more lives than the proverbial cat. It consistently refuses to stay dead. Not only did it come to life again just a few years later, but it has been periodically resurrected every few years since, and the Channel Tunnel Companies are in existence today. In the fall of 1887, Gladstone brought all the force of his powerful oratory to bear in a speech favoring the tunnel. In return, he was promptly and savagely attacked by *The Times* of London—and just as emphatically endorsed by some others. The project was now marking time, pending British permission to proceed. Nothing more has been accomplished on construction since, although there have been occasional revivals of the project, and inspections have been made of the work which terminated in 1883. The bores driven through the chalk from each shore and extending a considerable distance under the sea had been sealed up. Despite the lapse of time, *they had remained dry when inspected several years after abandonment*, and the chalk surface seemed actually to be hardening from the effects of this exposure to air. Thus the matter lay for some more years, despite efforts to revive it.

*Revived during the World War.*

During the World War, the tunnel project came to the fore again. Paradoxical though it seems, this time war served as an argument *for* instead of against the tunnel. The creation of such a tunnel, it was pointed out, would have been of inestimable advantage to the British Army in its support of the French. Thus a Committee of the House of Commons was again appointed to investigate the project. On July 28, 1916, this Committee entertained a party of French for the purpose of discussing a revival of the scheme, upon which no work had been done since 1883. Plans were being somewhat revised by this time. Two parallel tubes (each to be eighteen and a half feet inside) would be used, with cross connections for ventilation purposes. The total length of the double-tube tunnel was to be some twenty-seven miles, including the lengthy underground sections on each side of the Channel. A ten-foot-diameter pilot tunnel was to be bored first, and the tunnels were to be lined with concrete, Again, nothing constructive resulted. British insularity once more triumphed over the promoters of the tunnel, and again the project slid back into another period of obscurity. But once more it proved to be only temporary, for in 1924 the matter came up again—although only to meet another defeat. On July 7 of that year Prime Minister Ramsay MacDonald announced that the government had again decided against the tunnel project.

The lapse of activity that followed this last decision was considerably shorter than that following some earlier defeats. For, in May of 1929, the daily press reported that the government had set up a special committee to inquire into the economic aspects of the "proposed Channel Tunnel." And, in March of 1930, this Tunnel Committee electrified the nation by issuing a report that recommended the construction of a twin-tube tunnel. The practicability of a main tunnel was to be determined from the results of boring a pilot tunnel, which would cost about $27,160,000. If this was successful, two eighteen-and-a-half-foot railway tubes, thirty-six miles long, were to be constructed at an additional cost of $121,120,000—making a total of $154,500,000 for the entire project by the time that approaches and tracks were added. The Channel Tunnel Companies were still in existence and still retained the backing of two important railroads. About twenty-four miles of this projected tunnel was to be under the sea, and the remaining twelve miles would be under land. The water ranged from 120 to 200 feet in depth, and investigations still indicated that the chalk bed under the Channel extended completely across it.

### The Tunnel Lies Dormant Again.

Nothing more has transpired since that last report was made, and most people now consider the matter closed. Indeed, *The Times*, on March 15, 1930, discussed it in a very sceptical vein, closing with: "It seems more than likely that the last word about the tunnel has been said by a Committee which will be recorded as having reported in its favour." Perhaps so. But if its record of the past seventy-odd years can be taken as any criterion, it may yet be too soon to regard the English Channel Tunnel as a dead issue. Last objections were applied toward the great cost and the difficulty of making this venture pay its way. Yet its estimated cost is only about fifty per cent over the actual cost of the Pennsylvania Railroad's "New York tunnels and terminal"; it is much below the cost of the Colorado River Aqueduct and less than a third the cost of the Panama Canal. In the face of such knowledge, it behooves one to be rather cautious about predicting that the English Channel Tunnel will never be built or that it will never pay to build it. Some people think otherwise, and, even if their cost estimates should prove too optimistic, the tunnel advocates still have a project as promising as some others that have been carried into execution elsewhere in the past. Much more difficult engineering works have been accomplished and the Channel Tunnel may not yet be a dead issue. And who knows but that the day may yet come when the Simplon-Orient Express, speeding westward towards the French coast, will veer slightly from its present course, heading through the greatest tunnel in history to end its trip right in the heart of London instead of at the boat dock of Calais. For, in the language of the parliamentarian, the Channel Tunnel still remains on the table as "unfinished business."

# Index

235